THE
Atomic Age
OPENS

PREPARED
BY THE EDITORS OF
Pocket BOOKS

Pocket BOOKS, Inc.

NEW YORK, N. Y.

The Atomic Age Opens

Published by Pocket BOOKS, Inc., August, 1945

1st printing, August, 1945

GENERAL EDITOR
    Donald Porter Geddes

SCIENCE EDITOR
    Gerald Wendt

ASSISTANT EDITORS
    James Mitchell Clark, Helen D.
    Livingston, Mary E. Marquette,
    Thelma Sargent, Arnold Mitchell,
    Charles H. Schnell, Matilda Berg

DESIGNER
    Ernst Reichl

CONTENTS

On August 6, 1945, a bomb was dropped on the city of
Hiroshima, and the Atomic Age opened

President Truman's statement that an atomic bomb had
been dropped on Japan was in itself enough to set the
world agog, but when a further statement from Secretary
Stimson revealed what the test bomb had done in New
Mexico, and the Army in the Pacific told what this new
weapon had done to Hiroshima, public curiosity instantaneously became universal concern.

Having, after grave consideration, used it as a weapon of
destruction for the sole purpose of shortening the agony
of war, the President said that the knowledge, itself an
awful responsibility, would be kept secret until such time
as it could be revealed with the certainty that it would
be used solely for preserving peace and working for the
improvement of mankind. People everywhere voiced their
concern and their opinions, and many wondered if mankind could be trusted with such power.

What is it? How did they do it? What does it mean?
Never before had so many non-scientists sought understanding of a technical subject.

Recognizing the necessity for the widest possible understanding of what atomic energy is and how man has
finally succeeded in harnessing it, Pocket BOOKS commis-
sioned Dr. Gerald Wendt, well-known physicist and author,
to prepare this part of the book, which contains a full
account and layman's explanation of every important step
in the research up to the outbreak of war, and also an
account of such information as the Army has released on
the atomic bomb itself.

The Meaning of the Challenge   158

Meanwhile, in every corner of the land, in every country
on the globe, men began to sense the enormity of the
challenge this new force made. Here were the means,
should they get in the hands of wrong-minded men, of
conquering the world, even of destroying it. Here, on the
other hand, was the power that would do all work, and
permit of a veritable Utopia.

Which will it be? Can man ever again survive war?
And finally, can we prevent another war? These are the
questions that are concerning all men now that the Atomic
Age is here.

. . . on the ninth day of the Atomic Age,
Japan surrendered

...

Man Had Divided the Indivisible

THE RISE OF CIVILIZATION has been marked by man's ability to comprehend and overcome the secrets of nature and the problems of his environment. Each step in his harnessing and controlling of elemental forces—water, fire, the minerals of the earth—has brought a change in his habits of work and his ways of living. But no matter how revolutionary the development, men are never content with progress made. It is the progress still to be made that constitutes the challenge to thinkers, that makes mankind's civilization a kinetic and vital thing.

No greater mystery or more fantastic dream than the discovery of the source of the energy of the sun has ever challenged mankind. Since the days of the alchemists, even from the days of the great philosophers of the ancient world, the hope of transmuting elements and of unlocking the basic secret of nature has intrigued and stimulated visionaries and scientists. Deeper and deeper into the very nature of nature itself has man peered, until finally he reached the point where he was dealing with things so small as to be indiscernible. The quest, however, went on, because the secret of nature was still hidden. Meanwhile, as man's knowledge of infinitesimal things became greater, his knowledge also of the infinity of the universe expanded, until a mere handful were convinced of a world and a series of worlds large beyond knowing or even comprehending, all motivated and held in place in an appointed scheme by a force hidden and locked in the atom, believed to be the smallest unit of matter. And it was within this unit that scientists, looking at things no man could ever see, became convinced that the heat of the sun and the energy that made all things go was locked. If this energy could be unleashed, man would have such power as would make work as we have known it unnecessary. He might even have power enough to destroy himself and his world.

Now this basic force, this secret of the sun, this energy beyond all comprehension, this power to revolutionize man's way of living, has been found. The indivisible atom has been split, and mankind stands at the threshold of a future no one can foresee. The scientists have given us a new world in which there will be order or chaos as we will have it. The chaos will be easily obtainable; in fact it will be inevitable if this new force is not controlled by a new sense of social responsibility that will equal the dangers. Man is no longer playing with Chinese fire-crackers which at the worst can only burn local fingers and start isolated fires. He is now beginning a road that may take him to a point where he can harness the sun to do his bidding.

This book has been prepared for the purpose of ex-plaining to non-scientists how this power is obtained, where it lies in nature, and how omnipresent and inex-haustible it is, and also for the purpose of showing the nature and extent of public reaction to this astounding discovery.

The nuclear physicists have opened the Atomic Age and have thereby imposed upon every thinking human being—not just upon sociologists and politicians—the vital necessity of making those adjustments in thinking, in laws, in ways of life, in human relationships, that will prevent the chaos and give mankind instead a future golden and peaceful.

Buildings and People

Disappeared

The World Was Told

AT 10:45 a.m. on August 6, 1945, the most closely guarded secret of the war was first given to the world in utmost solemnity by President Truman in a dispatch to the United States. In this, as in the other official announcements, there is a sobering awareness of the tremendous responsibility involved.

Sixteen hours ago an American airplane dropped one bomb on Hiroshima, an important Japanese Army base. That bomb had more power than 20,000 tons of TNT. It had more than two thousand times the blast power of the British "Grand Slam" which is the largest bomb ever yet used in the history of warfare.

The Japanese began the war from the air at Pearl Harbor. They have been repaid manyfold. And the end is not yet. With this bomb we have now added a new and revolutionary increase in destruction to supplement the growing power of our armed forces. In their present form these bombs are now in production and even more powerful forms are in development.

It is an atomic bomb. It is a harnessing of the basic power of the universe. The force from which the sun draws its powers has been loosed against those who brought war to the Far East.

Before 1939, it was the accepted belief of scientists

that it was theoretically possible to release atomic energy. But no one knew any practical method of doing it. By 1942, however, we knew that the Germans were working feverishly to find a way to add atomic energy to the other engines of war with which they hoped to enslave the world. But they failed. We may be grateful to Providence that the Germans got the V-1's and the V-2's late and in limited quantities and even more grateful that they did not get the atomic bomb at all.

The battle of the laboratories held fateful risks for us as well as the battles of the air, land and sea, and we have now won the battle of the laboratories as we have won the other battles.

Beginning in 1940, before Pearl Harbor, scientific knowledge useful in war was pooled between the United States and Great Britain, and many priceless helps to our victories have come from that arrangement. Under that general policy the research on the atomic bomb was begun. With American and British scientists working together, we entered the race of discovery against the Germans.

The United States had available a large number of scientists of distinction in the many needed areas of knowledge. It had the tremendous industrial and financial resources necessary for the project and they could be devoted to it without undue impairment of other vital war work. In the United States the laboratory work and the production plants, on which a substantial start had already been made, would be out of reach of enemy bombing, while at the time Britain was exposed to constant air attack and was still threatened with the possibility of invasion.

For these reasons Prime Minister Churchill and President Roosevelt agreed that it was wise to carry on the project here. We now have two great plants and many lesser works devoted to the production of atomic power.

Employment during peak construction numbered 125,-
000, and over 65,000 individuals are even now engaged in
operating the plants. Many have worked there for two
and a half years. Few know what they have been producing. They see great quantities of material going in and
they see nothing coming out of these plants, for the
physical size of the explosive charge is exceedingly small.
We have spent two billion dollars on the greatest scientific gamble in history—and won.

The Greatest Marvel

But the greatest marvel is not the size of the enterprise,
its secrecy, or its cost, but the achievement of scientific
brains in putting together infinitely complex pieces of
knowledge held by many men in different fields of science into a workable plan. And hardly less marvelous has
been the capacity of industry to design, and of labor to
operate, the machines and methods to do things never
done before so that the brain child of many minds came
forth in physical shape and performed as it was supposed
to do.

Both science and industry worked under the direction
of the United States Army, which achieved a unique success in managing so diverse a problem in the advancement of knowledge in an amazingly short time. It is
doubtful if such another combination could be got together in the world. What has been done is the greatest
achievement of organized science in history. It was done
under high pressure and without failure.

We are now prepared to obliterate more rapidly and
completely every productive enterprise the Japanese have
above ground in any city. We shall destroy their docks,
their factories, and their communications. Let there be
no mistake; we shall completely destroy Japan's power
to make war.

It was to spare the Japanese people from utter destruction that the ultimatum of July 26 was issued at Potsdam. Their leaders promptly rejected that ultimatum. If they do not now accept our terms they may expect a rain of ruin from the air, the like of which has never been seen on this earth. Behind this air attack will follow sea and land forces in such numbers and power as they have not yet seen and with the fighting skill of which they are already well aware.

The Secretary of War, who has kept in personal touch with all phases of the project, will immediately make public a statement giving further details.

His statement will give facts concerning the sites at Oak Ridge, near Knoxville, Tennessee, and at Richland, near Pasco, Washington, and an installation near Santa Fé, New Mexico. Although the workers at the sites have been making materials to be used in producing the greatest destructive force in history, they have not themselves been in danger beyond that of many other occupations, for the utmost care has been taken for their safety.

The fact that we can release atomic energy ushers in a new era in man's understanding of nature's forces. Atomic energy may, in the future, supplement the power that now comes from coal, oil, and falling water, but at present it cannot be produced on a basis to compete with them commercially. Before that comes there must be a long period of intensive research.

It has never been the habit of the scientists of this country or the policy of this Government to withhold from the world scientific knowledge. Normally, therefore, everything about the work with atomic energy would be made public.

But under present circumstances it is not intended to divulge the terminal processes of production or all the military applications, pending further examination of possible methods of protecting us and the rest of the world from the danger of sudden destruction.

I shall recommend that the Congress of the United States consider promptly the establishment of an appropriate commission to control the production and use of atomic power within the United States. I shall give further consideration and make further recommendations to the Congress as to how atomic power can become a powerful and forceful influence toward the maintenance of world peace.

From London the statement prepared by former Prime Minister Winston Churchill was released to the Associated Press by Prime Minister Clement Attlee, with an introductory statement by Mr. Attlee.

Mr. Attlee's Introduction

Everybody will have seen the important statements which have been made by President Truman and by Mr. Stimson, the United States Secretary for War, about the atomic bomb. The problems of the release of energy by atomic fission have been solved and an atomic bomb has been dropped on Japan by the United States Army Air Force.

President Truman and Mr. Stimson have described in their statements the nature and vast implications of this new discovery. Some account is now required of the part which this country has played in the remarkable scientific advances which have now come to fruition. Before the change of Government, Mr. Churchill had prepared the statement which follows and I am now issuing it in the form in which he wrote it.

Mr. Churchill's Statement

By the year 1939 it had become widely recognized among scientists of many nations that the release of energy by atomic fission was a possibility. The problems which remained to be solved before this possibility could be turned into practical achievement were, however, manifold and immense, and few scientists would at that time have ventured to predict that an atomic bomb could be ready for use by 1945.

Nevertheless, the potentialities of the project were so great that His Majesty's Government thought it right that research should be carried on in spite of the many competing claims on our scientific manpower. At this stage the research was carried out mainly in our universities, principally Oxford, Cambridge, London (Imperial College), Liverpool, and Birmingham.

At the time of the formation of the coalition Government, responsibility for co-ordinating the work and pressing it forward lay in the Ministry of Aircraft Production, advised by a committee of leading scientists presided over by Sir George Thomson.

At the same time, under the general arrangements then in force for the pooling of scientific information, there was a full interchange of ideas between the scientists carrying out this work in the United Kingdom and those in the United States.

Such progress was made that by the summer of 1941 Sir George Thomson's committee was able to report that in their view there was reasonable chance that an atomic bomb could be produced before the end of the war.

At the end of August, 1941, Lord Cherwell, whose duty it was to keep me informed on all these and other technical developments, reported that substantial progress was being made. The general responsibility for the scientific research carried on under the various technical committees lay with the then Lord President of the Council, Sir John Anderson.

In these circumstances, having in mind also the effect of ordinary high explosive, which we had recently experienced, I referred the matter on August 30, 1941, to the chiefs of staff committee in the following minutes:

"General [Sir Hastings] Ismay, for chiefs of staff committee.

"Although personally I am quite content with the existing explosives, I feel we must not stand in the path of improvement and I therefore think that action should be taken in the sense proposed by Lord Cherwell and that the Cabinet Minister responsible should be Sir John Anderson.

"I shall be glad to know what the chiefs of the staff committee think."

The chiefs of the staff recommended immediate action with the maximum priority. . . . Full use was also made of university and industrial laboratories.

On October 11, 1941, President Roosevelt sent me a letter suggesting that any extended efforts on this important matter might usefully be co-ordinated or even jointly conducted. Accordingly, all British and American efforts were joined and a number of British scientists concerned proceeded to the United States. Apart from these contacts, complete secrecy guarded all these activities and no single person was informed whose work was not indispensable to progress.

By the summer of 1942 this expanded program of research had confirmed with surer and broader foundations the promising forecasts which had been made a year earlier and the time had come when a decision must be made whether or not to proceed with the construction of large-scale production plants.

Meanwhile it had become apparent from the preliminary experiments that these plants would have to be on something like the vast scale described in the American statements which have been published today.

Great Britain at this period was fully extended in war production and we could not afford such grave interference with the current munitions program on which our warlike operations depended.

Moreover, Great Britain was in easy range of German bombers and the risk of raiders from the sea or air could not be ignored. The United States, however, where parallel or similar progress had been made, was free from these dangers. The decision was therefore taken to build the full-scale production plants in America.

Arrangements for Cooperation

In the United States the erection of the immense plants was placed under the responsibility of Mr. Stimson, United States Secretary of War, and the American Army administration, whose wonderful work and marvelous secrecy cannot be sufficiently admired. The main practical effort and virtually the whole of its prodigious cost now fell on the United States authorities, who were assisted by a number of British scientists. The relationship of the British and American contributions was regulated by discussion between the late President Roosevelt and myself, and a combined policy committee was set up.

The Canadian Government, whose contribution was most valuable, provided both indispensable raw material for the project as a whole and also necessary facilities for the work on one section of the project, which has been carried out in Canada by the three Governments in partnership.

The smoothness with which the arrangements for cooperation which were made in 1943 have been carried into effect is a happy augury for our future relations and reflects great credit on all concerned—on the members of the combined policy committee which we set up, on the enthusiasm with which our scientists and technicians gave of their best, particularly Sir James Chadwick, who gave up his work at Liverpool to serve as technical adviser to the United Kingdom members of the policy committee and spared no effort, and, not the least, on the generous spirit with which the whole United States organization welcomed our men and made it possible for them to make their contribution.

By God's mercy, British and American science outpaced all German efforts. These were on a considerable scale but far behind. The possession of these powers by the Germans at any time might have altered the result of the war and profound anxiety was felt by those who were informed.

Every effort was made by our intelligence service and by the Air Force to locate in Germany anything resembling the plants which were being created in the United States. In the winter of 1942-43 most gallant attacks were made in Norway on two occasions by small parties of volunteers from the British Commandos and Norwegian forces at heavy loss of life, upon stores of what is called "heavy water," an element in one of the possible processes.

The second of these two attacks was completely successful.

The whole burden of execution, including the setting up of the plants and many technical processes connected therewith in the practical sphere, constitutes one of the greatest triumphs of American—or indeed human—genius of which there is record.

Moreover, the decision to make these enormous expenditures upon a project which, however hopefully established by American and British research, remained nevertheless a heart-shaking risk stands to the everlasting honor of President Roosevelt and his advisers.

It is now for Japan to realize in the glare of the first atomic bomb which has smitten her what the consequence will be of an indefinite continuance of this terrible means of maintaining a rule of law in the world.

This revelation of the secrets of nature long mercifully withheld from man should arouse the most solemn reflections in the mind and conscience of every human be-

ing capable of comprehension. We must indeed pray that
these awful agencies will be made to conduce to peace
among the nations and that, instead of wreaking meas-
ureless havoc upon the entire globe, they may become a
perennial foundation of world prosperity.

Atom Bomb Razes 60 Per Cent of Hiroshima

FOUR AND one-tenth square miles, "or 60 percent" of
Hiroshima were wiped out by the devastating atomic
bomb dropped at 9 a. m., August 6, by a B-29, United
States Army Strategic Air Forces headquarters reported
today in an Associated Press dispatch.

Five major industrial targets were wiped out in the
city of six and nine-tenths square miles.

"Additional damage was shown outside the completely
destroyed area," said a communiqué based on reconnaissance photographs made over the city of 343,000 persons
on the morning of the day the bomb was dropped by a
Superfortress which felt the concussion of the parachute-
dropped weapon ten miles away. The bomb, which
crashed with the explosive power of 20,000 tons of TNT,
covered the entire area in two minutes with a black
cloud which "looked like boiling dust" and climbed 40,-
000 feet, according to W. H. Lawrence, writing in the
New York Times.

That smoke cloud, visible as much as 160 miles at
sea, still hung over the city four hours later and thus far
has prevented any photographic record of the undoubted
tremendous damage caused by the explosion of the war's
greatest secret weapon.

[Crewmen of a reconnaissance Superfortress flying over
Wakayama Prefecture at a point 170 miles from Hiroshima reported that they could see the flash of the bomb
as well as the smoke, the United Press reported. "A tremendous flash like a ball of fire or a setting sun shone
in the distance," the pilot said.]

The Greatest Story of the War

That was the story told today by the daring men who had charge of the first use of this tremendous agent of destruction. They were Captain William S. Parsons, 44, of Chicago, who described himself as the "weaponeer" and is a naval ordnance expert who designed the bomb in which the energy of the split atom was channelized, and Colonel Paul W. Tibbet, Jr., of Miami, Florida, pilot of the Superfortress *Enola Gay*.

They told this, the greatest story of the war, with an air that was almost casual. They described simply the reaction they observed as the bomb was dropped, but they made no precise claims of damage resulting, preferring to let that wait for detailed photographic reconnaissance.

"When the bomb dropped we put as much distance between ourselves and the ball of fire as we could," Captain Parsons said. "In our desert experiments at about dawn there had been a blinding flash when the first one exploded, but yesterday, in the bright sunlight, the flash was not so great.

"I heaved a sigh of relief because I knew the bomb was a success. We felt the first concussion about one minute after the bomb hit, and within another minute or two a great black cloud of boiling dust and churning debris was 1,000 feet off the ground and above it while smoke climbed like a mushroom to 20,000 feet. A few fires were visible around the edges of the smoke, but we could see nothing of the city except the dock area, where buildings were falling down."

Captain Parsons was asked for his reaction, as the designer of the bomb, at the moment when its destructive terror was unleashed on the city and the people below. He said he had no particular reaction except that of relief when the great flash signified that the bomb had exploded.

Until the bomb was released only Captain Parsons, Colonel Tibbet and the bombardier, Major Thomas W. Ferebee of Mocksville, North Carolina, knew the exact purpose of the mission. The others of the crew, who had been selected carefully, knew that they were on an unusual mission of great importance but not that the greatest contribution to the science of warfare since the invention of gunpowder was in the bomb bays below.

Some of them ejaculated "My God" and few could believe their eyes when the great black cloud covered the city of 343,000 from the impact of a single bomb in a matter of seconds.

Captain Parsons remarked wryly that it probably was a good idea for the "weaponeer" to go along on the first battle mission on which his product was to be used because it gave him a great personal interest in making certain that the bomb he had designed could be used safely. . . .

Although the technique of employing the bomb is not yet perfected, Captain Parsons said that it was important that the first one should be dropped as quickly as possible "because this weapon is worth so much in terms of shortening the war."

When the bomb was dropped, Colonel Tibbet said, he banked sharply in a 270-degree turn, his motors turning over as fast as possible so the plane would be out of the area where the great blast would be felt.

Colonel Tibbet was asked what effect the concussion had on the plane. He said it was so slight that it seemed merely to be a burst of anti-aircraft fire that exploded near by. The airplane was not shaken as much by the blast as it would have been by thermal updrafts from incendiary attack on a Japanese city at low level.

Two other men who played an important role in the development of this weapon, Rear Admiral William R. Purnell of Bowling Green, Missouri, and Brigadier General Thomas F. Farrell of Albany, New York, were on hand for the first mission and at today's conference.

General Farrell said that the Allied command's fear that the Germans would beat us to the secret of utilizing the atom as a means of destruction impelled General Spaatz to send large forces of Flying Fortresses and Liberators to destroy the town of Oranienburg, near Berlin, site of highly developed German experiments with bombs. That raid set the Germans back by years, General Farrell said.

Colonel Tibbet disclosed in a United Press dispatch that Hiroshima was selected as the target only when the plane had made a landfall over Japan.

It Was Hard to Believe What We Saw

After the bomb had been released, he said, "it was hard to believe what we saw. Below us, rising rapidly, was a tremendous black cloud. Nothing was visible where only minutes before the outline of the city, its streets and buildings and waterfront piers were clearly apparent.

"It happened so fast we couldn't see anything and could only feel the heat from the flash and the concussion from the blast.

"There were a couple of sharp slaps against the airplane. It felt like close bursts of flak. I yelled a warning to the crewmen, but we were all okay."

Visual shock was apparent from several miles, Colonel Tibbet remarked. "What had been Hiroshima was going up in a mountain of smoke," he continued. "First I could see a mushroom of boiling dust—apparently with some debris in it—up to 20,000 feet. The boiling continued three or four minutes as I watched. Then a white cloud plumed upward from the center to some 40,000 feet. An angry dust cloud spread all around the city. There were fires on the fringes of the city, apparently burning as buildings crumbled and the gas mains broke."

Stimson's Account of the Bomb

The recent use of the atomic bomb over Japan, which was today made known by the President, is the culmination of years of herculean effort on the part of science and industry working in co-operation with the military authorities. This development, which was carried forward by the many thousand participants with the utmost energy and the very highest sense of national duty, with the greatest secrecy and the most imperative of time schedules, probably represents the greatest achievement of the combined efforts of science, industry, labor, and the military in all history.

The military weapon which has been forged from the products of this vast undertaking has an explosive force such as to stagger the imagination. . . . The scientists are confident that over a period of many years atomic bombs may well be developed which will be very much more powerful than the atomic bombs now at hand. . . .

The requirements of security do not permit of any revelation at this time of the exact methods by which the bombs are produced or of the nature of their action. However, in accord with its policy of keeping the people of the nation as completely informed as is consistent with national security, the War Department wishes to make known at this time, at least in broad dimension, the story behind this tremendous weapon which has been developed so effectively to hasten the end of the war. Other statements will be released which will give further details concerning the scientific and production aspects of the project and will give proper recognition to the scientists, technicians, and the men of industry and labor who have made this weapon possible.

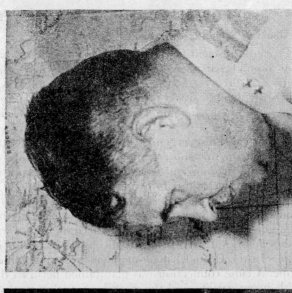

MAJOR GENERAL LESLIE RICHARD GROVES

DR. VANNEVAR BUSH

The Chain of Scientific Discoveries

The chain of scientific discoveries which has led to the atomic bomb began at the turn of the century when radio-activity was discovered. Until 1939 work in this field was world wide, being carried on particularly in the United States, the United Kingdom, Germany, France, Italy, and Denmark.

. . . The war, however, ended the exchange of scientific information on this subject and, with the exception of the United Kingdom and Canada the status of work in this field in other countries is not fully known. . . .

A large number of American scientists were pressing forward the boundaries of scientific knowledge in this fertile new field at the time when American science was mobilized for war. Work on atomic fission was also in progress in the United Kingdom when the war began in Europe. A close connection was maintained between the British investigations and the work here, with a pooling of information on this as on other matters of scientific research of importance for military purposes. . . .

No Praise Is Too Great

Late in 1939 the possibility of using atomic energy for military purposes was brought to the attention of President Roosevelt. He appointed a committee to survey the problem. Research which had been conducted on a small scale with Navy funds was put on a full-scale basis as a result of the recommendations of various scientific committees. At the end of 1941 the decision was made to go all-out on research work, and the project was put under the direction of a group of eminent American scientists in the office of Scientific Research and Development, with all projects in operation being placed under contract with the O. S. R. D. Dr. Vannevar Bush, director of O. S. R. D., reported directly to the President on major developments. Meanwhile, President Roosevelt appointed a general policy group, which consisted of former Vice-President Henry A. Wallace, Secretary of War Henry L. Stimson, General George C. Marshall, Dr. James B. Conant, and Dr. Bush.

In June, 1942, this group recommended a great expansion of the work and the transfer of the major part of the program to the War Department. Major General Leslie R. Groves was appointed by the Secretary of War to take complete executive charge of the program and . . . the President's general policy group appointed a military policy committee consisting of Dr. Conant, as his alternate, Lieutenant General Wilhelm D. Styer, and Rear Admiral William R. Purnell. . . .

Although there were numerous unsolved problems concerning the several theoretically possible methods of producing explosive material, nevertheless, in view of the tremendous pressure of time it was decided in December, 1942, to proceed with the construction of large scale plants. Two of these are located at the Clinton Engineer Works in Tennessee and a third is located at the Hanford Engineer Works in the State of Washington. The decision to embark on large-scale production at such an early stage was, of course, a gamble, but as is so necessary in war a calculated risk was taken and the risk paid off. . . .

A special laboratory dealing with the many technical problems involved in putting the components together into an effective bomb is located in an isolated area in the vicinity of Santa Fé, New Mexico. This laboratory has been planned, organized and directed by Dr. J. Robert Oppenheimer. The development of the bomb itself has been largely due to his genius and the inspiration and leadership he has given to his associates.

Certain other manufacturing plants much smaller in scale are located in the United States and in Canada for essential production of needed materials. Laboratories at the Universities of Columbia, Chicago, and California, Iowa State College, and at other schools as well as certain industrial laboratories have contributed materially in carrying on research and in developing special equipment, materials, and processes for the project. A laboratory has been established in Canada and a pilot plant for the manufacture of material is being built.

This work is being carried on by the Canadian government with assistance from, and appropriate liaison with, the United States and the United Kingdom. . . .

Behind the concrete achievements [of the many industrial concerns which have contributed so signally to the success of the project] lie the tremendous contributions of American science. No praise is too great for the unstinting efforts, brilliant achievements, and complete devotion to the national interest of the scientists of this country. Nowhere else in the world has science performed so successfully in time of war. All the men of science who have co-operated effectively with industry and the military authorities in bringing the project to fruition merit the very highest expression of gratitude from the people of the nation.

In the War Department the main responsibility for the successful prosecution of the program rests with Major General Leslie R. Groves. His record of performance in securing the effective development of this weapon for our armed forces in so short a period of time has been truly outstanding and merits the very highest commendation.

Extraordinary Secrecy

From the outset extraordinary secrecy and security measures have surrounded the project. This was personally ordered by President Roosevelt, and his orders have been strictly complied with. The work has been completely compartmentalized so that while many thousands of people have been associated with the program in one way or another, no one has been given more information concerning it than was absolutely necessary to his particular job. As a result only a few highly placed persons in government and science know the entire story. It was inevitable, of course, that public curiosity would be aroused concerning so large a project and that citizens would make inquiries of members of Congress. In such instances the members of Congress have been most cooperative and have accepted in good faith the statement of the War Department that military security precluded any disclosure of detailed information. . . .

Because it has not been possible for Congress to keep a close check on the expenditure of the funds appropriated for the project which to June 30, 1945, amounted to $1,950,000,000, key scientific phases of the work have been reviewed from time to time by eminently qualified scientists and industrial leaders in order to be certain that the expenditures were warranted by the potentialities of the program.

The press and radio of the nation, as in so many other instances, have complied wholeheartedly with the requests of the Office of Censorship that publicity on any phase of this subject be suppressed. . . .

Prompt Action

It was early recognized that in order to make certain that this tremendous weapon would not fall into the hands of the enemy, prompt action should be taken to control patents in the field and to secure control over the ore which is indispensable to the process. Substantial patent control has been accomplished in the United States, the United Kingdom, and Canada. In each country all personnel engaged in the work, both scientific and industrial, are required to assign their entire rights to any inventions in this field to their respective governments.

Arrangements have been made for appropriate patent exchange in instances where inventions are made by nationals of one country working in the territory of another. . . .

At the present stage of development of the science of atomic fission, uranium is the ore essential to the production of the weapon. Steps have been taken, and continue to be taken, to assure us of adequate supplies of this mineral.

Great Promise

Atomic fission holds great promise for sweeping development by which our civilization may be enriched when peace comes, but the overriding necessities of war have precluded the full exploration of peace-time applications of this new knowledge. With the evidence presently at hand, however, it appears inevitable that many useful contributions to the well-being of mankind will ultimately flow from these discoveries when the world situation makes it possible for science and industry to concentrate on these aspects. . . .

Already in the course of producing one of the elements much energy is being released, not explosively but in regulated amounts. This energy, however, is in the form of heat at a temperature too low to make practicable the operation of a conventional power plant. It will be a matter of such further research and development to design machines for the conversion of atomic energy into useful power. How long this will take no one can predict but it will certainly be a period of many years. Furthermore, there are many economic considerations to be taken into account before we can say to what extent atomic energy will supplement coal, oil, and water as fundamental sources of power in industry in this or any other country.

We are at the threshold of a new industrial art which

will take many years and much expenditure of money to develop.

Because of the widespread knowledge and interest in this subject even before the war, there is no possibility of avoiding the risks inherent in this knowledge by any long-term policy of secrecy. Mindful of these considerations as well as the grave problems that arise concerning the control of the weapon and the implications of this science for the peace of the world, the Secretary of War, with the approval of the President, has appointed an interim committee to consider these matters. . . .

The committee is charged with the responsibility of formulating recommendations to the President concerning the post-war organization that should be established to direct and control the future course of the United States in this field both with regard to the research and development aspects of the entire field and to its military applications. It will make recommendations with regard to the problems of both national and international control. In its consideration of these questions, the committee has had the benefit of the views of the scientists who have participated in the project. . . . Every effort is being bent toward assuring that this weapon and the new field of science that stands behind it will be employed wisely in the interests of the security of peace-loving nations and the well-being of the world.

New Mexico—The First Test

AT 5:30 a.m., July 16, the first atomic explosion created by man caused a blast which was seen and felt by observers within a three hundred mile range of Alamogordo Air Base, remote desert scene in New Mexico, which had been chosen for the test. The steel tower from which the atomic bomb was suspended disappeared, leaving a gaping crater, and plate glass windows in Silver City, 100 miles away, were shattered.

A few days before the test, key advisers Major General Leslie R. Groves, Dr. Vannevar Bush, and Dr. James B. Conant had assembled to watch scientists complete the bomb and hoist it upon the steel tower. At 3 a.m. of July 16, they gathered at shelters more than five miles from the tower. "Minus 20 minutes, minus 15 minutes," counted the announcer above the thunderstorm which raged outside the shelters where tense men awaited the results of their years of labor. At "minus 45 seconds" a robot mechanism took over control. Observers outside the shelter were knocked down by the pressure wave which followed the dazzling flash of light given off by the explosion. An enormous cloud, rising 40,000 feet into the air, obscured the scene of destruction loosed by the men within the control tower.

Brigadier General Thomas A. Farrell, in relating his impressions of the event, said:

The lighting effects beggar description. The whole country was lighted by a searing light with the intensity many times that of the midday sun. It was golden, purple, violet, gray, and blue. It lighted every peak, crevasse and ridge of the near-by mountain range with a clarity and beauty that cannot be described but must be seen to be imagined. It was that beauty the great poets dream about but describe most poorly and inadequately.

Thirty seconds after the explosion came first the air blast pressing hard against the people and things, to be followed almost immediately by the strong sustained, awesome roar which warned of doomsday and made us feel that we puny things were blasphemous to dare tamper with the forces heretofore reserved to the Almighty. Words are inadequate tools for the job of acquainting those not present with the physical, mental, and psychological effects. It had to be witnessed to be realized.

DR. J. ROBERT OPPENHEIMER

ISIDOR ISAAC RABI

A Tremendous Burst of Light

General Farrell went on to describe the scene in the shelter:

In that brief instant in the New Mexico desert the tremendous effort of the brains and brawn of all these people came suddenly and startlingly to the fullest fruition. Dr. (J. R.) Oppenheimer (director of the atomic bomb laboratory in New Mexico), upon whom had rested a heavy burden, grew tenser as the last seconds ticked off. He scarcely breathed. He held onto a post to steady himself. For the last few seconds he stared dreamily ahead and then when the announcer shouted 'Now!' and there came this tremendous burst of light followed shortly thereafter by the deep growling roar of the explosion, his face relaxed into an expression of tremendous relief. Several of the observers standing back of the shelter to watch the lighting effects were knocked flat by the blast.

Dr. Kistiakowsky (an assistant to the director) threw his arms around Dr. Oppenheimer and embraced him with shouts of glee. Others were equally enthusiastic. All the pent-up emotions were released in those few minutes and all seemed to sense immediately that the explosion had far exceeded the most optimistic expectations and wildest hopes of the scientists. All seemed to feel that they had been present at the birth of a new age—The age of Atomic Energy—and felt their profound responsibility to help in guiding into right channels the tremendous forces which had been unlocked for the first time in history. . . .

No matter what might happen now all knew that the impossible scientific job had been done. . . . There was a feeling in that shelter that those concerned with its nativity should dedicate their lives to the mission that it always be used for good and never for evil.

What the Bomb Did

WHAT HAPPENED at Hiroshima was at first obscured by an impenetrable cloud of dust and smoke. But gradually reports of the terrible destruction began to filter through.

Homer Bigart of the *New York Herald Tribune* wirelessed the following description from Okinawa.

The atomic bomb which devastated Hiroshima may have killed at least 200,000 of the city's 313,000 population, according to conservative estimates of photograph interpreters after several hours' study of reconnaissance photos taken by Lieutenant General Ennis C. Whitehead's 5th Air Force.

It was stressed that this casualty estimate was based solely on visible havoc and did not include death or injury from atomic rays released by the bomb. The photographs were brilliantly clear. They showed persons moving in the outskirts of the town and a train with steam up in the marshaling yards about a mile from the center of impact of the bomb in the heart of the city. This was a matter of interest since scientists had warned that the lethal effect of the atomic blast might linger for many hours.

Not all of Hiroshima was leveled by the blast. Industrial buildings around the perimeter of the ten-square-mile city were still standing, as were the docks and harbor installations north of the city. The main double-track coastal railroad from Tokyo to Shimonoseki was buried under drifted rubble in at least three places but the marshaling yards to the southwest seemed relatively intact. Rows of freight cars were still standing in the yards.

But four and a half square miles of the heart of Hiroshima were so completely pulverized that General George C. Kenney, commanding Allied air forces in the Far East, remarked that the town seemed to have been ground into dust by a giant foot. In this area it seemed hardly credible that anyone could have escaped death. Building fronts had fallen across streets, obliterating all but the widest thoroughfares which now appeared as narrow lanes hardly discernible in the photos. About six reinforced concrete buildings had withstood the shock.

Hiroshima, in its sudden death, looked utterly unlike the Japanese cities ravaged by previous raids. There were no bomb craters. There was no evidence of widespread conflagration, only traces of two small fires.

Mac R. Johnson, also of the *New York Herald Tribune*, reported from Guam on the interpretation of photographs studied by the staff of General Carl A. Spaatz.

When An Atomic Bomb Explodes

Reconnaissance photographs showed that 4.1 square miles, or 60 per cent of the city's built-up area of 6.9 square miles, were completely destroyed. Five major industrial targets within this area were destroyed, while additional damage was shown outside the completely destroyed area.

Photographs of the seaport of Hiroshima, 420 miles south of Tokyo on southern Honshu, gave the first evidence of what happens when an atomic bomb explodes. The photographs were taken Monday afternoon, presumably six to eight hours after the bomb exploded, and by that time only a few small fires were burning and the smoke had cleared, permitting excellent photographs to be taken.

The atomic bomb apparently fell somewhere in about the exact geographical center of Hiroshima, and for two to three miles in every direction, fire had completely burned and leveled every building, finally burning itself out in the outskirts of the city.

Photographs showed only a few concrete buildings protruding here and there from the white and black ashes. Since fires had wiped out the area of explosion there was nothing left to indicate what might have been the blast damage before the flames consumed every shred of combustible material.

The conflagration was so intense that fire leaped, or was hurled, across six major natural firebreaks and three or more man-made fire barriers by the tremendous blasting force of the atomic bomb, which creates heat of solar intensity. The major firebreaks are rivers, streams, or canals from 100 to 300 yards wide, while the Japanese, in anticipation of incendiary attacks, had cleared buildings from wide strips of land through the city in creating other barriers to prevent the spreading of fire.

One 20th Air Force photographic interpreter was asked how large a force of Superfortresses carrying ordinary incendiary bombs would have to be used to cause the same widespread destruction by fire. He said the comparison was hard to make because "with one match and a seventy-knot wind you might have been able to burn it down, or perhaps 120 to 150 Superforts scoring excellent hits in strategic places could have done it."

But he added that the atomic bomb did not need either good wind or good luck—it accomplished the greatest damage ever inflicted on a city by one plane with one bomb, and equalled what would have been a major accomplishment by a massed force of B-29's.

He said that the loss of life among the Japanese in Hiroshima presumably was tremendous, and he added that an enemy broadcast had admitted it was considerable.

Oblique photographs taken at the time the atomic bomb exploded showed the entire city completely obscured by a dome of thick, black smoke or dust, while rising in a pillar from the city to a height of 40,000 feet was boiling, swirling white smoke. The photograph interpreter said the black smoke could have been "industrial dust"—dust which for years has accumulated atop buildings and on the ground, and which was suddenly stirred up and arose in a cloud as the bomb exploded. The white column of smoke, he said, was similar to the smoke and gas which billows up after any heavy explosion, such as an ammunition ship exploding.

The photographs did not show any damage other than that which one would expect to see after a normal incendiary attack. In other words, burned-out Hiroshima looked like any other city which had been destroyed by fire in a B-29 incendiary assault. There was no evidence of any crater or blast damage, although it is entirely possible that large sections of the city were knocked flat by the exploding missile, and fire subsequently consumed the flattened structures. However, long, low air-raid shelters seemed untouched by the blast and skeletons of concrete buildings still remained erect in the ashes.

A Most Awesome Sight

A Japanese soldier happened to be staying in a hotel in Hiroshima on the day of the attack. This is his account of what happened, as given by the Associated Press.

"I looked up," he said. "Simultaneously a lightning-like flash covered the whole sky, blinding my eyes. Unconsciously, I dived for cover and a torn quilt miraculously was blown over me, which I hugged to myself for dear life.

"Several minutes later I was outside. All around I found dead and wounded. Some were bloated and scorched—such an awesome sight. Their legs and bodies stripped of clothes and burned with a huge blister.

"All green vegetation from grasses to trees perished in that period. It was the most awesome sight I have ever witnessed."

The official Japanese account of the bombing was broadcast in French and directed to Europe.

Listeners were told that "as a consequence of the use of the new bomb against the town of Hiroshima on August 6, most of the town has been completely destroyed and there are numerous wounded among the population.

"The destructive power of these bombs is indescribable," the broadcast continued, "and the cruel sight resulting from the attack is so impressive that one cannot distinguish between men and women killed by the fire. The corpses are too numerous to be counted.

"The destructive power of this new bomb spreads over a large area. People who were outdoors at the time of the explosion were burned alive by high temperature while those who were indoors were crushed by falling buildings."

The *Asahi Shimbun* made a strong editorial appeal to the people of Japan to remain calm in facing the use of the new type bomb and renew pledges to continue to fight.

The Whole World Gasped

WITH THE COMING of the first news of the attack upon Hiroshima and of the new power that had been unleashed for better or for worse, the world could talk of little else. As Don Goddard, NBC news commentator, said in his broadcast on August 7th,

". . . no single development of this generation, at least, has so stirred the imagination of men. All the leading editorials of the world are playing upon this theme today. Military and Naval authorities, scientists and just plain citizens like ourselves, are wondering and talking. All shades of opinion are expressed and all manner of predictions made."

President Truman Voiced His Reaction

When President Truman voiced his reaction in his address to the nation on August 10th, he spoke as a citizen whose mind and imagination were staggered by the import of the news, but he spoke, too, as one who had had forewarning and foreknowledge of this epochal opening of the atomic age, and who had considered its import.

I realize the tragic significance of the atomic bomb.

Its production and its use were not lightly undertaken by this Government. But we knew that our enemies were on the search for it. We know now how close they were to finding it. And we knew the disaster which would come to this nation, to all peaceful nations, to all civilization, if they had found it first.

That is why we felt compelled to undertake the long and uncertain and costly labor of discovery and production.

We won the race of discovery against the Germans.

Having found the bomb, we have used it. We have used it against those who attacked us without warning at Pearl Harbor, against those who have starved and beaten and executed American prisoners of war, against those who have abandoned all pretense of obeying international laws of warfare. We have used it in order to shorten the agony of war, in order to save the lives of thousands and thousands of young Americans.

We shall continue to use it until we completely destroy Japan's power to make war. Only a Japanese surrender will stop us.

The atomic bomb is too dangerous to be loose in a lawless world. That is why Great Britain and the United States, who have the secret of its production, do not intend to reveal the secret until means have been found to control the bomb so as to protect ourselves and the rest of the world from the danger of total destruction.

As far back as last May, Secretary of War Stimson, at my suggestion, appointed a committee, upon which Secretary of State Byrnes served as my personal representative, to prepare plans for the future control of this bomb. I shall ask the Congress to co-operate to the end that its production and use be controlled, and that its power be made an overwhelming influence toward world peace.

We must constitute ourselves trustees of this new force —to prevent its misuse and to turn it into the channels of service to mankind.

It is an awful responsibility which has come to us.

We thank God that it has come to us instead of to our

enemies; and we pray that He may guide us to use it in His ways and for His purposes.

To those who, unlike the President, had of necessity been kept uninformed of the close reality of the atomic age, who had considered it always a subject for Superman cartoons and wild-eyed fantasy, or at best a project for the 25th century, the whole view of the multiple implications that man's splitting of the atom would have was difficult to obtain at the beginning. Some thought, with the President, of the tragic significance of the bomb. Others exulted that we had "won the race of discovery against the Germans." For many the first impulse was to say, "This is our secret. Let's hold on to it." Military strategists considered the effect upon what remained of the Second World War and upon the possibility of waging war in the future. Political thinkers realized the need for international co-operations and control to make atomic power, in the President's words, "an overwhelming influence toward world peace." A mosaic of the opinions voiced by world leaders and your next door neighbor, by a taxi driver and the country's outstanding editorial writers, formed a picture of decent people thinking together along much the same lines as the President, and grasping for solid ideas through the haze of the first excitement.

The Tragic Significance

The editors of the *New York Herald Tribune* expressed the immediate consciousness of the release of a strange, terrible, and unpredictable power.

If President Truman's anouncement yesterday means all that it seems it may ultimately mean, it is not only the most important single announcement in the course of the war; it is an announcement more fateful for human history than the whole war itself. The victory or defeat of armies, the fate of nations, the rise or fall of empires are all alike, in any long perspective only the ripples on the surface of history; but the practicable unlocking of the inconceivable energy of the atom would stir history itself to its deepest depths.

Yet, here is President Truman's flat statement that on Sunday an American airplane dropped a single small bomb on the city of Hiroshima which exploded with the power of 20,000 tons of TNT, with a blast effect equivalent to that of all the high explosive which could be carried in a fleet of 2,000 B-29's. Hiroshima is still reported lost under an impenetrable cloud of smoke and dust, rendering any assessment of the damage impossible. The statement is weird, incredible and somehow disturbing; one forgets the effect on Japan or on the course of the war as one senses the foundations of one's own universe trembling a little. It is as if the gruesome fantasies of the "comic" strips were actually coming true. It is as if we had put our hands upon the levers of a power too strange, too terrible, too unpredictable in all its possible consequences for any rejoicing over the immediate consequences of its employment.

How the Japanese, who now see it leveled directly against them and their cities, may feel about it one can only guess. Neither they nor our own public yet know in what quantities this frightful weapon can be manufactured, what may be its full destructive scope, to what ruin it may reduce Japan before this war is over. If it proves decisive for the present war, however, that will be only the beginning. This extraordinary triumph of scientific research is still of purely destructive application; as such it must profoundly affect all issues of international politics and war. But beyond that there is the even more profoundly revolutionary possibility that the atoms can be utilized directly as a new source of constructive energy.

As to that, one may only speculate until more information is vouchsafed concerning the whole astounding enterprise. But whatever strange futures may be opening before us, one must devoutly hope that mankind, which has shown the curiosity and cleverness to make this new advance into the dread mysteries of nature, can also show the wisdom to employ the powers he has grasped for some other end than self-extinction.

The Omaha *Morning World-Herald,* in an editorial entitled "We Are Not Proud of It," spoke for the many men and women who felt a certain conviction that war is a dirty business, that it is not easy to reconcile military necessity and decent instincts.

A salesman interviewed by a *PM* reporter said, "All a person can say is that it's terrific—it's world-shaking. I don't think the human mind can grasp everything it can do." . . . A taxi driver from Brooklyn and a clerk were two of the many who prayed that this soul-stirring discovery might not fall into the wrong hands. . . . The Peoples Lobby, Inc., was reported by the *New York World Telegram* to be calling for a ban on the use of atomic bombs in future wars. All over the country, people wrote letters to the editors of their newspapers, protesting the killing of the noncombatant civilians in Japan, calling it inhuman, and protesting our disregard of moral values. In Britain, too, where the news of the atomic bomb topped all other news, the letter columns were full of such expressions as "In the name of humanity, let us stop and ask ourselves where we are marching?"

To Shorten the Agony of War

There was, however, another face to the immediate reaction, which accepted the horror as a necessity in view of Japan's fanatic actions. The *New York Times,* in its editorial "Our Answer to Japan," discussed in a matter-of-fact way the bomb as answer to a military problem.

The American answer to Japan's contemptuous rejection of the Allied surrender ultimatum of July 26 has now been delivered upon Japanese soil in the shape of a new weapon of destruction which unleashes against it the forces of the universe, which revolutionizes warfare as thoroughly as did the introduction of gunpowder in the age of bows and arrows, and which gives a new and awesome meaning to the Allied threat to apply military power until "the utter devastation of the Japanese homeland." What every military man has dreamed of, what Hitler frantically searched for to the last, what thousands of scientists worked upon in a mad race in the rival laboratories—the decisive "secret weapon," the magic key to victory—has been found in America and is now ready to be hurled against our enemies.

That weapon is the atomic bomb, the product of combined American and British ingenuity, the reward of a $2,000,000,000 scientific gamble which we won—a bomb which surpasses in explosive force 20,000 tons of TNT, which is two thousand times more powerful than the biggest of the bombs that leveled Germany.

So far only one of these bombs has been dropped on Japan, just to demonstrate its power. It was unloosed over Hiroshima, on the Japanese main island, and that enemy army base immediately went up in an "impenetrable cloud of dust and smoke." That is but a sample of what is in store for all Japan. For these bombs are no longer experiments. They are in mass production, with 65,000 workers employed on them in three different plants, and even more powerful bombs are on the way. So fearful are its effects that Allied leaders are themselves reluctant to use it and once again extend to Japan the chance to end the war on the terms of the ultimatum. But if their war leaders are still so blind as to persist in the rejection of our mercy, they may expect, as President Truman says, "a rain of ruin from the air the like of which has never been seen on this earth."

The new bomb, which is the crowning demonstration of Allied technical, scientific and material superiority over the enemy, has in effect put the Japanese war lords of this day in the same position in which their Samurai ancestors found themselves on the arrival of Commodore Perry's "black ships" off Tokyo in 1853. At that time, confronted with a fighting power which they could not match, and despite all the prayers to their gods for the annihilation of the "barbarians," the Japanese leaders decided for a peace which lasted until Pearl Harbor. It remains to be seen whether the descendants of the Samurai are equally wise or whether they prefer to sacrifice the nation to their fanaticism.

The editor of the *Hartford Daily Courant* held the same viewpoint.

We cannot disregard the voice of our own consciences, which tells us that the new bomb is just as bestial and inhuman as the Japanese say it is. . . . Even so it is difficult to reach any conclusion except that we must use the atomic bomb in all its fury to press this insane bloodletting to the end that is inevitable anyway just as swiftly as possible. After all, the bomb differs only in degree, and not in kind, from the other instruments of warfare in common use. . . . The basic fact is that war is by nature blind, stupid, inhumane, and utterly immoral. It is difficult to play the gentleman about fighting it. The humane man does not leave innocent women and children maimed and screaming under the wrecks of their blitzed houses in London, or in Berlin or Munich or Frankfurt either, for that matter. The humane man does not shatter the body of the American boy, whose only wish is to stay on the home farm, as he wades ashore at Saipan. The humane man does not make war at Pearl Harbor without warning, to let American sailors, immured in the sunken hulk of a battleship, die of starvation and suffocation after sixteen lingering days.

No, it is not against the awe-inspiring lethal might of the atomic bomb that our horror should be directed, but against war itself. . . . And when victory comes, then let us stand together with all men of good will, no matter what cultural, social, or political gaps divide us, to strive with God's help that the bestiality that is war shall never be let loose among men again.

President Truman, too, in his address to the nation, answered those who decried the bombing of innocent civilians, and who begged that a second atomic bomb be withheld.

The world will note that the first bomb was dropped on Hiroshima, a military base. That was because we wished in this first attack to avoid, insofar as possible, the killing of civilians. But that attack is only a warning of things to come. If Japan does not surrender, bombs will have to be dropped on war industries and, unfortunately, thousands of civilian lives will be lost. I urge Japanese civilians to leave industrial cities immediately, and save themselves from destruction.

When Maxwell Anderson, the noted playwright, was asked by *PM* for his reaction to the news, he spoke for the parents of the country in words that bore out the President's voice of determination: "My first reaction was an obvious one. I have two sons in service, and I hoped the bomb would help shorten the war. But," he added, "at the same time I felt a great apprehensiveness. This new bomb, you know, is a very dangerous plaything for civilization."

Reveal the Secret?

Because of the widespread realization that the bomb is "a dangerous plaything," and that it was only by God's grace that we, rather than our enemies, were the first to be able to use it, many people insisted that this secret should be kept. In a public opinion poll taken by the *New York Journal-American,* a lawyer said, "This is one formula the Government must retain, because this would be civilization's only protection against totalitarian delusionists who want to run the world." A Private First Class agreed that "our Government should keep the secret."

In Washington, however, sharp division of opinion developed in Congress over the question of whether the secret of the atomic bomb should be kept from the rest of the world.

Some Senators predicted it would have to be made public ultimately, and suggested the United Nations organizations, charged with keeping the peace, be made the custodian.

Senator O'Mahoney of Wyoming said the world could not permanently be deprived of the benefits of the discovery, especially as to its use for peaceful pursuits.

Senator Capper of Kansas, ranking minority member of the Senate Foreign Relations Committee, urged the United States keep the secret, at least for a time.

Elsewhere in the world there were voices that dissented on keeping the secret for the United States and Great Britain. Palmer Hoyt, Portland, Oregon, newspaper publisher and former domestic director of the

Office of War Information, said in an Associated Press dispatch:

When we entered yesterday into the atomic age, it became vital that the peoples of the earth be given the immediate opportunity to understand each other through the medium of the world-wide flow of free information.

There is only one thing that can save civilization, and that is the unhampered release of objective news—American style—among the nations. It will no longer be possible for part of the world to be informed, part kept in ignorance.

Professor J. B. S. Haldane, one of Britain's leading scientists, said that atom power would have to be nationalized in the United States and elsewhere.

OUR Atomic Bomb

PM, in an editorial entitled "Thank God, It's OUR Atomic Bomb," summed up the reasons for not keeping it exclusively "ours."

To know what the end of the world is like one must live through it, not perish with it. That seeming impossibility is what is happening to us today—happening, that is, to all except the thousands of Japanese who vanish into vapor at the falling of our atomic bomb.

OUR atomic bomb! Do we realize, can we realize, what that little possessive pronoun means?

Three little letters, *o-u-r,* to reflect the thankfulness of all Americans and of their allies that Germany or Japan did not produce this engine of inconceivable destruction.

Three little letters, *o-u-r,* to represent the power of one nation, if it chooses to misuse that power, to control the world and wreck it.

Three little letters, *o-u-r,* to show who among the peoples of the world must say first, and perhaps finally, whether the power of the atom shall be used for the welfare or the extermination of man.

Those same three letters, *o-u-r*, are the symbol not only of derivation and possession, but also of property ownership. Who is to utter, in this last sense, the word they spell? Will it be spoken by humanity? By the American people? Or by the owners of chemical plants, by bankers, by promoters of international cartels, by those who measure everything in science, everything in the world, in terms of money and of power over men?

Today the splitting atom is the ingredient of an engine of war—an engine so terrible that it gives the world but two alternatives: *the end of war or the end of humanity*.

"We the people of the United States" cannot hold this weapon to ourselves. We cannot use it, after the Japanese are defeated, like a new constitutional preamble to secure the blessings of liberty to ourselves and our posterity. What we control today, all nations will possess tomorrow, and the killing power of the smallest of them will be multiplied 20,000 times.

The atomic bomb is a weapon of surprise. It is not today, and cannot be tomorrow, a competitive weapon of pre-armed nations. Against it there is no defense, there can be none, except to use it first. In war, as we have known it in modern history—competitive war between prepared nations—it has no place except to dig a crater deep and broad enough to bury man and all his works.

So, if we expect the atomic bomb to remain a weapon of war in a world of future wars, the only safe and sensible course is to use it now to exterminate or subjugate everybody else on earth. That would be Hitler's choice, Japan's choice. It is not the American choice. But choosing otherwise, we must have the wisdom to see that a simple choice is not enough. America must join and lead in a worldwide renunciation of this weapon by a worldwide renunciation and prevention of war.

That is one reason why the world is coming to an end, and why we have a chance to share in its rebirth.

Another world is dying, too, the world of lesser mechanical and natural marvels, and the society built upon them. This will come more slowly, but it will come. The atomic bomb has burst in stunning suddenness as an agent of destruction. The splitting atom will be more leisurely adapted to the arts of peace, but it will be adapted. Today, this product of man's genius is what the first horseless carriage was in the evolution of the automobile and airplane.

What will happen to industry, to society, when the power of all the coal mined in a year is compressed into an exploding fistful of atoms? What will happen to society, to human relations, to human dignity, if that power is given into the keeping of any smaller group than the whole people themselves?

Ominous words, because faintly reassuring, were heard in Washington yesterday. "Substantial patent rights," it is said by the War Department, have been assured to the American and British Governments through their participation in the development of this discovery. What does that mean except that other "substantial patent rights" have been retained by American or British chemical companies that may have been concerned in the development?

An Anglo-American chemical cartel, even without the aid of a denazified I. G. Farbenindustrie, no doubt can build a pleasant world of semi-leisure for the millions whose work and pay envelopes will be lightened by this inconceivable new agency of mechanical power. Is that the kind of control over their destiny that men and women are hungering for? If it is, we might as well turn the world over to future war lords and let them blow it up.

There have been many "moments of destiny" in human history. If that phrase were used now for the first time, in all the pristine power of its wording, it would still be inadequate to express the responsibility that rests upon the human race today, most heavily of all upon the American people and their Government.

We are compelled, at one step, to bridge the gap between the scientific genius which produced this marvel, and the social sluggishness which has made lesser marvels a too-great tax upon our powers of adjustment.

There is no escape. The split atom may shatter humanity, but not before then will it retreat into the physical void from which it came.

The dust of creation is in our hands. We must master it. We must make it the servant of mankind, the servant of peace, the instrument by which man proves his right to rule that part of the universe in which he has his being.

An Overwhelming Influence Toward World Peace

Perhaps one of the most widespread reactions was the belief that another war would mean world suicide. War's potentialities had become so terrible that no nation could afford to provoke another to open hostilities. The *New York Times,* in an editorial entitled "Atomic-Bomb Shudders," said in part:

An international conference of the kind proposed by Secretary Stimson ought to be held. Much good may come from it. If conferees shudder enough at the prospect of another war in which rocket-propelled atomic bombs will be directed at hapless cities across whole continents and oceans they ought also to shudder at high explosives, sixteen-inch naval guns, land mines, torpedoes, and the rest of war's horrible paraphernalia. In a word, the trail may be blazed for disarmament and peace. Whether or not anything will come of this shuddering remains to be seen. The House of Commons shuddered when Kitchener mowed down the hordes of the Mad Mullah in the Sudan during a battle in which the machine gun was first used, and some members even proposed that the weapon be outlawed. But the machine gun is still used. In the fifteenth century Leonardo and Tartaglia shuddered at the thought of what their own military inventions would do —to no avail. If this time the shuddering produces more tangible results, the invention of the atomic bomb was worth the two billions that it cost.

Bishop William T. Manning of the Protestant Episcopal Diocese of New York said, according to the Associated Press:

The development of the atomic bomb is one of the greatest events of all time in the world of science and in human life as well as in warfare. It makes absolutely imperative the ending of war.

This discovery gives man a frightful power for evil but also an unprecedented power for good. If the faith and conscience of mankind are correspondingly awakened by this mighty event, a new day of hope will open for the world.

Even the former masters of the German machine foresaw a revolution in world politics resulting from the introduction of the atomic bomb into warfare by the United States, according to Drew Middleton writing in the *New York Times*.

Paradoxically, it was German Foreign Minister Joachim von Ribbentrop, a man who soon will be charged as a war criminal involved in the greatest crime of all—starting the second World War—who sounded the most hopeful note.

"No one would be so stupid as to start a war now," he said. "It is the opportunity for mankind to end war forever."

A Necessary Future Objective

With peace the necessary future objective in everyone's mind, there seemed to be two approaches to the method of keeping peace—approaches that might be classified as the negative and the positive. On the negative, "Thou shalt not" side were the suggestions for atomic power as a big stick to be wielded by the Security Council of the United Nations. The *New York Herald Tribune* suggested in an editorial:

Perhaps war has, indeed, been rendered at last too costly in life and civilization for peoples to face it any longer. Here, if peace is to be saved, one must obviously combine the atomic bomb with the political invention of the Charter of the United Nations. The new weapon may well serve to strengthen greatly the forces of civilization which will line up behind the Charter; for unless its use is strictly controlled by the Security Council, in the interest of the whole world, man will live under the gravest threats of disaster. If uranium is the sole source of unstable atoms, then the deposits of that element must be policed, sales licensed and laboratories inspected in the interest of all.

Retained in the hands of the Security Council as a potential punitive weapon, the bomb would have a terrific deterrent effect. No nation would be likely to pursue forbidden courses if it knew that a couple of airplanes could next day obliterate the heart of its capital city. But only the passage of time and the secure establishment of the Charter as an effective instrument could make these results certain. Reduction of armies and navies to police proportions might then follow. At this point one is already beyond the field of purely military calculation; the ultimate question is that of the political wisdom with which the world of the future is to be governed.

Senator Carl Hatch of New Mexico also emphasized the need for strengthening the United Nations peace machinery, although for him the atomic bomb was the incentive rather than the instrument. As reported by the United Press, he called for prompt action to give the world court compulsory jurisdiction over international disputes.

"We simply have two alternatives—to live together peacefully or die together," he said in an interview.

"I'm no scientist, but I imagine this is merely a crude form of what can be developed," he added. "The possibilities transcend the imagination."

On the positive side of the ledger of peace were predictions of international co-operation that might result from the example of scientific co-operation utilized in splitting the atom, and from the fact that this enormous possession must be shared. Mrs. Franklin Delano Roosevelt, widow of the late President, said in an NBC broadcast that:

One thing we must all remember is that this discovery was made by the pooling of many minds belonging to different races and different religions, that the way the work was done sets the pattern for the way in which in the future we may be able to work out our difficulties—not by setting up superior races, but by learning to co-operate and using the best that each one has to contribute to solve the problems of this new age.

Thanks to Hitler

The *New York Times*, in an editorial entitled "Thanks to Hitler," reviewed the extent of the "pooling of many minds" that Mrs. Roosevelt mentioned.

"By God's mercy British and American science out-paced all German efforts," said Winston Churchill in his comments on the atomic bomb, thereby confirming Washington's statement that the Germans were not far behind us. Though the credit for having forestalled the Germans must go to the air forces that bombed German research laboratories where secret weapons were developed, we have some reason to thank Hitler and Mussolini for handicapping themselves. The Fuehrer's irrational glorification of Nordics and Il Duce's acceptance of the Nuremberg policy had the result of presenting us with some of the best physicists of Germany and Italy and of occupied countries.

Consider the galaxy of scientific stars that shine in the American atomic-bomb firmament. "Thanks for having forced Dr. Lise Meitner to flee to Stockholm," we say to Hitler, when we recall that she played her part in blazing the trail that led to the release of energy from the uranium atom. "And thanks for Niels Bohr, who, though a Dane, was unacceptable to you under your Nuremberg laws and who formulated the theory on which the atomic bomb is based." That man Bohr was a godsend, one of the leaders in the group that worked here on the bomb. "Thanks, too, for Einstein," who was also consulted and who gave us the simple equation that showed just what the relation of matter to energy is and how one can be converted into the other. And then there is Enrico Fermi. "What a mistake you made, Il Duce, when you obligingly toed Hitler's Nordic mark and forced him out." He was Italy's foremost physicist, this Fermi, the man who showed how easily a slow neutron can slip into an atom, to burst its nucleus and release the terrific energy that laid Hiroshima low. A priceless gift was he to the group that developed the bomb. There must be scores of others who were not mentioned in the official announcements—engineers, technicians, chemists, physicists of distinction,

DR. LISE MEITNER

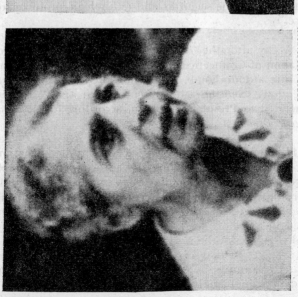

DR. ENRICO FERMI

all gifts of Hitler and Mussolini. Great Britain receives
our thanks for different reasons. Her case was a whole-
hearted willingness to pool the knowledge of experts,
just as she did in the case of jet-propulsion.

There has never been a more striking example of international co-operation in science than that presented by
the development of the bomb. Is this to be the end? Are
we to lapse into the old more or less nationalistic pursuit
of science when great issues are at stake? Why can't there
be international co-operation in dealing with arthritis,
cancer, hormones, vitamins or, for that matter, with the
whole field of science? Apart from the overwhelming
social potentialities of utilizing atomic energy we shall
have learned little socially if we do not apply the system
of organization, planning, and direction that gave us the
bomb to solve the scientific and technologic problems of
peace.

A day after the *Times* editorial Senator Brien Mc-
Mahon of Connecticut, motivated by the development
of the atomic bomb, which he called "the most stupendous scientific achievement of our time," recommended to President Truman, according to the *New
York Times:*

"That he propose to the United Nations the formation
of a group, similiar in scope and ability to that formed
to work on the atomic bomb, and to provide for a central
co-ordinated direction of such a group to the end that the
united energies of the scientists of the world be combined in an effort to discover causes and cures for the
deadly diseases of the world."

He suggested that knowledge acquired through co-ordinated planning should be used to "help mankind instead of ruin mankind."

The *Berkshire County Eagle* in Pittsfield, Massachusetts, looked forward to a discovery of cheap power that would minimize the advantage of nations with great resources, and so eliminate an economic cause of war. The *Sioux City Journal* in Iowa saw fear as a motive for keeping peace. Perhaps, then, the outlook is bright after all for world peace that everyone dreams of, that every paper across the country, from Louisiana to Rhode Island, from Massachusetts to Texas took as its editorial text for days following the opening of the atomic age.

An Awful Responsibility Has Come to Us

Sir John Anderson, the Cabinet Minister under whose direction British research and development proceeded, said: "We've opened a door. It is yet to be seen what's on the other side of that door—maybe a treasure-house, maybe only the realization of a maniac's dream of destruction." Also in Britain, H. G. Wells, who forecast atomic bombs twelve years ago in his book, *The Shape of Things to Come*, was quoted by the United Press as saying to his household: "This can wipe out everything bad—or good—in this world. It is up to the people to decide which."

The National Conference of Christians and Jews warned that the atomic bomb increases America's responsibility for assuring success of the United Nations organization.

"Moral forces no less spectacular must be released by Americans if the peoples of the world are to continue to look to us as their leader in reconversion to civilized living," the statement said.

The *New World*, official newspaper of the Catholic archdiocese of Chicago, called the atomic bomb the most crucial test to which Christianity has ever been submitted, and warned that:

The bomb itself will not be able to guarantee peace but should prompt men to work harder than ever before for a just and peaceful world.

The magnitude of the responsibility that rests and shall rest upon the shoulders of those who have brought this force into being was everywhere the ultimate end of the thinking and the reaction to atomic fission and its results.

The *New York Herald Tribune* saw the solemnity of our position:

The reports from Hiroshima are now available. They seem to put beyond question the stark and still hardly credible fact that this country possesses a small instrument which, when dropped in a suitably dense population center, can instantly annihilate some 100,000 human beings. It is a fact which Americans have received with no sense of exultation. There is no satisfaction in the thought that an American air crew has produced what must without doubt be the greatest simultaneous slaughter in the whole history of mankind, and even in its numbers matches the more methodical mass butcheries of the Nazis or of the ancients. There is only a very solemn sense of the inadequacy of man's social and political equipment for meeting the responsibility entailed by the possession of so terrible an instrument of physical power. . . .

This blast at Hiroshima may open a new scientific age. But it should also drive home the fact that in the understanding and control of human psychology, human behavior, there lies the greatest unexplored field for inquiry. Its promise is very rich; and it is certain that if we are to survive our own triumphs over the physical world we must drive relentlessly forward to an understanding of the mental one.

Scientific and Political Revolution

And the *New York Times* outlined the steps that must be taken to modernize our thinking and bring it up to our scientific development.

The bomb that dropped on Hiroshima was doubtless heard by human ears for hundreds of miles around, but morally it was heard around the world. Its implications for good or evil are so tremendous in so many directions that it will take months before our minds can really began to envisage them. Today men can only think haphazardly of a few of its possible consequences: the effect on the war against Japan, the effect on the future of all warfare, the peacetime applications to power and economic creation, the scientific and political revolution that it must bring.

For a revolution in science and a revolution in warfare have occurred on the same day. Atomic energy released a bomb that has more than two thousand times the blast power of any bomb previously used in the history of warfare—all this, and the enormous secret preparations that went into it, read like some incredible fiction. But in the bewilderment that such a stupendous announcement must bring, one consequence stands clear. Civilization and humanity can now survive only if there is a revolution in mankind's political thinking.

Since the Industrial Revolution that began about two centuries ago and has developed at an accelerative pace, each great war has been more disastrous than its predecessors. But this fact has still not prevented mankind from resorting to war for the settlement of differences. It did not affect the childish and irresponsible minds of the

Mussolinis and Hitlers. With the horrible prospect of utter annihilation opened by the atomic bomb, it is hard to imagine how the people of any nation on earth can possibly want another war.

But can mankind grow up quickly enough to win the race between civilization and disaster? Or will new would-be conquerors arise who will see in the atomic bomb merely the certain means for the instant realization of their dreams? Will they whisper to their own people, or the few whom they choose to take into their confidence, that they will be perfectly safe, and the new war will be over immediately, if only they get in the first blow? Will they, by suppression, the concentration camp, torture and the firing squad, be able to drag their people into war regardless of how their people feel about it? These are the possibilities that mankind must now forever prevent.

If we are to do so we must change our accustomed ways of thinking far more rapidly than we have ever had to change them before. It is fortunate, indeed, that this country has already ratified the United Nations Charter. But it is more obvious than it ever was that this is only a first step. Tremendous tasks remain to be done without loss of time. We must begin systematically to reduce, and eliminate if possible, all the chief causes of war. We must carry on the battle against international trade barriers, and still more against the twisted economic reasoning that leads to the creation of such trade barriers. We must extend the geographical range of democracy. We must bring every pressure that we can to confine or eliminate dictatorships and despotisms wherever they may exist in the world.

We must do this not primarily for the sake of the people who live under these despotisms, important as that consideration is, but primarily for the protection of the rest of the world. We must assume that no people will want war if they realize what its consequences with the atomic bomb will be. All that we have to fear, in that case, is that a totalitarian government, by suppressing information and free discussion, by feeding its own people on a propaganda of lies, will prevent its people from knowing the facts until it is too late, while it plots secretly against the rest of the world. Wherever the press and information and discussion are free, wherever the facts are known and the government is really the choice of a liberated people, that people will want peace and can force its government to keep the peace.

But the atomic bomb is already here. The mentality and the national and world political institutions necessary to make certain that mankind gets only the immense benefits, and not the unthinkable destruction, that this great discovery can bring, must be created without delay.

ACME

View of University of Illinois atom smasher

The Search for Understanding

What Did Happen

THE UNIVERSAL IMPRESSION that sixth day of August, 1945 was: This is it! To Japan it meant disaster, defeat, utter catastrophe. To United States soldiers it meant survival and home. To humanitarians it was a resurgence in awful form of the age-old question of the morality of mass murder. But even the impending end of the war, now assured, seemed small news compared with the terrific impact of what the new atomic bomb meant for humanity far above and beyond its value as a weapon. What did it mean? How did it happen? What would be its consequences in the years to come to industry, economics, education and the way people live. Civilians were dumbfounded. Scientists had known it was coming and, with better understanding, had feared the worst. The more aware they were of the possibilities of atomic energy, the more aghast were they at the problem of explaining it to their friends who suddenly wanted to learn all about atoms, electrons, and nuclei and to master chemistry and physics in a tense half-hour, after spurning them for years.

A new universe had indeed erupted into the world of men with the force of a volcano, with the brilliance of an exploding star. Strictly speaking, it was an old universe, older than man, than planets, perhaps even older than matter as we know it. In the atomic bomb for the first time man had employed the energy that lies deep within the atom, in its nucleus. It is the same source of energy that gives the sun its tremendous light and heat. Now complacency towards science and ignorance of the atom can no longer be excused. Here is force so tremendous that it must be understood.

The newspapers did their best, not only to report the event, but to stimulate speculation as to its meaning and to explain the science involved. But even Howard Blakeslee, competent science editor of the Associated Press, was handicapped by five years of secrecy. The work which had employed a large group of the best scientific minds of the country for nearly three years, which had cost two billion dollars, was still hidden by censorship. There was no explanation. Even the experts had to guess on the basis of atomic researches that were at least five years old. Most of the guesses were necessarily incorrect. Not until six days later, on Sunday, August 12, did the War Department release a fat book entitled "A General Account of the Development of Methods of Using Atomic Energy for Military Purposes Under the Auspices of the United States Government, 1940—1945." The story it told was almost as incredible as the bomb itself. To believe it, and certainly to understand it, required a much larger background of scientific knowledge than most people had.

The First Questions

There was first of all the question: What is an atom? Then a flood of questions: How do you know? Has anyone ever seen one? How do you mean, it explodes? Where does it get the power? Even the quick and infallible wisdom of radio commentators failed them in this crisis.

Such questions cannot be glibly answered. It is not hard to define an atom but it is very hard to make its reality convincing by words alone. The desperate ponderings of able men for centuries back had been needed to make the atom real—not to speak of many thousands of man-hours in the laboratory. No few columns of journalism could give the answer. A convincing answer requires a review of the slow growth of the basic concepts of matter and of energy—of chemistry and of physics. The briefest glance at them would show that "atomic" is not the right word to apply to this energy, this explosion and this age. The public grasped at the word as something vaguely familiar. Yet in truth, this new energy is no more atomic than is the energy of ordinary combustion or that of an electric battery. We have been using atoms throughout history, since all material things are made of them and every form of energy is tied to them. What makes this new energy distinctive is that it comes not from the weak and diffuse field of energy at the surface of the atom, but from the tautly packed, enormously concentrated storehouse within the atom's nucleus. It is, in truth, nuclear energy, not merely atomic.

It was developed by a small group of specialists in the field of nuclear physics, a science that was almost unknown and certainly unnamed twenty years ago. It grew out of the science of radioactivity when it became obvious that the explosion of radium atoms could not be accounted for by ordinary forces but must involve a concentrated cluster of matter and of energy at the very center of the atom. Twenty years ago the atom was no longer the "hard, massy particle" of Sir Isaac Newton's day, but had become as complex as the solar system, with electrons in orbits on the outside and the nucleus within. The advancing frontier of science had passed from the molecule to the atom a hundred years ago, from the atom to electrons and nuclei fifty years ago, then began to pry inside the nucleus twenty years ago. In 1939, the nucleus was cracked open, and behind the walls of military security, scouts are now rampant within the nucleus.

It was a group of Germans—Hahn, Meitner, Frisch and Strassmann—who in 1939 succeeded in breaking into the nucleus, shattering it into fragments and thus turning part of its matter directly into energy. Einstein was suddenly justified in his prediction of long ago that matter and energy are equivalent and can be transformed one into the other. It was unthinkable but it had been done. It was verified in Italy, in Denmark and in the United States. Because it had thereby been proved beyond all doubt, it was possible to organize and to finance a tremendous government project which sought to convert this nuclear energy into a new weapon of war. With the support of Dr. Vannevar Bush, Director of the Office of Scientific Research and Development, and under the direction of Dr. James B. Conant, Chairman of the National Defense Research Committee, the intrepid program went ahead with more money and speed than any previous research in history. On June 16 in New Mexico, a large-scale test proved that the answer was conclusive. The explosion was felt two hundred miles away and seen for more than a hundred miles. The atomic nucleus had erupted under the precise control of its inventors. The age of nuclear energy was born.

Incidental to this triumph was the creation—not the discovery—of two new chemical elements: plutonium and neptunium. They were unheard of before the war and their discovery would have been a sensation among chemists in normal times. Now they were created out of uranium by a step in transmutation that might have seemed miraculous but now is merely incidental to the vaster transmutation in the explosion itself. This is one of the wartime secrets that has been revealed. But in that world-capital of research in nuclear physics at Los Alamos, New Mexico, it is undoubtedly a minor item among much greater ones that are still kept secret. The War Department admits that only a portion of the story has been told—or ever can be told.

But the world at peace needs no more details; it needs to understand what is already in the news. The force of this atomic explosion is more than heat and pressure, more than anything material and physical. It is obviously the first impact of a social force greater than any that has struck the human race in two thousand years.

Every advance of science becomes a social force. We live as we do because of electricity and coal, automobiles and planes, telephones and radio. They are the products of science. Because of them and innumerable other inventions we have in the United States 130 million well-fed people in a land which once—without science—barely supported a few hundred thousand Indians. But all these technical developments have come gradually. Men, women, and especially children have been able to adjust their lives to them without understanding them. Most of them are foolproof. The atomic bomb is not.

So, suddenly every intelligent person wants to understand everything that is involved. This is a force that we can not leave to the experts nor to competitive development by industrial corporations. This is a force which was revealed by innocent philosophical research men and was made real by the highly organized effort of every available expert under complete control of the government itself. It belongs to the people. The people must understand it.

But understanding is not to be had by reading scattered accounts in the press nor even by studying a half dozen magazine articles. One cannot ask: What is the atomic bomb? The real questions are: What is the atom? What is energy? Why is the atom a source of energy? These are big questions, though they can be simply answered. In order to appreciate what atomic energy means it is first necessary to understand what ordinary energy is, where we have gotten it, how we have used it up to now.

Our Scientific Search

Energy—Up to Now

IT WAS ENERGY that erupted at Hiroshima, and energy more concentrated than had ever been known on earth before. But it was not pure, disembodied energy. When it struck buildings down it was the energy of tremendous air pressure. When it burned everything in reach it was the energy is enormous heat at a temperature of many thousands of degrees. But a few seconds earlier that energy had been concentrated and quiet within a small bomb. In each aspect the energy belonged to some form of matter. The two cannot be separated. They are tied together, on earth at least, and the essence of the problem is to understand the relation between them.

Both those words—matter and energy—are impossible to define, but everyone knows in general what they mean. We do not know what matter is "made of," but we do know that it occupies space, has inertia, attracts other matter with a force called gravity, and somehow it affects our senses so that we can see, feel, and taste it. It is the essence of things while energy is the essence of action. Anything that moves contains energy and gives it off when it is stopped. Anything that is stationary needs energy to set it into motion. When one is hit by a baseball, it is the matter that hits but it is the energy that hurts. On the other hand, it is not possible to throw a ball of pure energy, for energy must always be carried by something material. The only exceptions are perhaps the vibrations of light and heat and other rays that reach us across empty space from the sun and stars—and even there it is impossible to imagine vibrations without having something to vibrate, which is the reason, and the only reason, that scientists assume that empty space is filled with "ether."

Indestructible

Until these days of atom-smashing it was a basic principle of science that neither matter nor energy can ever be destroyed. Both change from one form to another, but the old idea was that there can be no change in the amount of matter or the amount of energy in the universe. That is no longer true. Back in 1905 a young patent office clerk in Switzerland named Albert Einstein developed a theory of relativity which involved the idea that under certain conditions matter could be changed into energy and energy into matter. According to that theory, a very small amount of matter would produce tremendous quantities of energy. But all this was theory and for fifteen years few paid any attention. Today it is a reality. That is the big news. To appreciate it one needs first to go back to the older common-sense ideas that matter and energy can both change into many forms but cannot be destroyed or changed into each other.

The changes of matter from one form to another are familiar. Materials from the soil and the air are changed into grass in the fields. The grass is eaten but its substance reappears in the body of a sheep. The sheep may become wool and mutton and these in turn become textiles or the flesh of a human being. The matter remains the same though its form changes. Even a fire does not consume matter. In the laboratory it is easy to show that the burning of a piece of wood or of a candle produces ash and gaseous products—carbon dioxide and water. The weight of the combustion products accounts for the entire weight of the substance that was burned. The substance has combined with oxygen in burning; it may have disappeared from human sight but it still exists, exactly the same quantity of matter as before.

DR. ALBERT EINSTEIN

Energy Changes

So also, energy can be changed from one form into another. The heat obtained from burning coal may convert
water into steam. The energy in the steam is the same as
that which was stored in the coal. The steam may then
be used in an engine and to give mechanical energy. The
moving pistons and wheels of a steam engine operate a
dynamo, perhaps, and the energy flows through it to be
converted into electricity, still another form of energy.
The electricity flows through a wire and may be used to
heat an electric light bulb or to turn a fan. Thus the
energy which came from the coal is transformed into heat
in the filament of the lamp and a part of it into light. In
the case of the fan the electricity is transformed into
mechanical energy and part of it into heating the motor.
Ultimately all of it goes into heat in our houses or factories and from them is radiated into the atmosphere
and thence into outer space. Energy is not destroyed. It is
merely changed from one form to another.

Energy in Motion

Everyone understands that energy means motion. It
take energy to throw a ball or propel an automobile. As
they get going they take on energy and they carry that
energy as long as they move. They give up the energy
when they stop. When brakes are applied to an automobile they slow it down, but the brakes get hot. The energy
of motion of the whole car has been transformed into
heat in the brakes.

But heat itself is a form of motion. The friction against
the brake-band converts the motion of the car into the
motion of the tiny particles that compose the brake-band,
known as molecules. The brake-band itself does not move,
but the molecules in it are stirred up into an intense
vibration which we call heat. If you touch the hot brake-

band the motion of its molecules strikes the nerves in your finger and makes them vibrate. Thus you feel the heat. And so the heat of any hot object is still the energy of motion: the vibrating motion of its molecules.

Pressure

When a gas is heated there is another effect. The difference between a gas and a solid is that in a gas the molecules are not held together but can separate from each other. They are always in motion, bouncing back and forth against each other. When a gas is heated the motion of the molecules gets faster. The collisions between them become more violent. So do the collisions with the walls of the container. And that is the cause of gas pressure. If the container is a cylinder with a piston at one end, the hot gases press against the piston and tend to push it out. In this way the heat energy of the burning gases in the cylinder of an automobile can be transformed into mechanical energy when the piston moves out, turns the crankshaft and moves the car forward. Whenever a gas is heated it either expands—if the walls will permit, or if there are no walls—or else the pressure increases. The higher the temperature, the greater the pressure.

Examples of these simple principles are familiar. Near a steam radiator the air of the room absorbs energy, gets hot, expands, therefore gets lighter, and so it rises to the ceiling of the room. In a cannon the powder charge explodes, forms large quantities of hot gas under high pressures, and the shell is forced out at high speed. The chief cause of rain and weather in all parts of the earth is the rising currents of light, hot air in the tropics and the descending currents of cold air toward the poles. The commonest examples however are the steam engine and the gasoline engine which provide industrial power by converting heat into pressure and pressure into motion.

Stored Energy

When a small boy pulls back the string of a bow or the rubber band of his slingshot, he is preparing to put energy into the arrow or the stone and put it in motion. But first he puts the energy into stretching the bowstring or the rubber sling. In that stretched form the bowstring contains energy. But it is not energy of motion. By pulling on it the boy has put energy into it, has stored energy in it. When he lets go, that stored energy is converted into the moving energy of the bow.

Energy can be stored in many forms. Mountain lakes are full of it. It was originally energy from the sun which was absorbed by water molecules out at sea. That energy evaporated the water, lifted it to the sky. Part of it was lost when the water fell as rain, but if the rain collected in a high reservoir it still contains much energy which will be released as it flows to the sea and can be captured and converted into electricity at a hydroelectric plant. The lake may look like a reservoir of water but actually it is a reservoir of energy—the energy that is stored in the water because of its height above sea level. In the textbooks this form of energy is called "potential energy." Anything lifted above the earth and capable of falling has some of it, which is converted into energy of motion as soon as it falls.

Chemical Energy

Man has made much use of the energy stored in the rain and in high places. Hydroelectric power is a very important source of industrial energy. But it is a cumbersome way of storing energy. Far more important to present civilization are the enormous amounts of energy that are stored not in the heights but in the depths of the earth, held there by chemical bonds. The most important form of stored energy is in coal and petroleum.

This too was originally energy that came directly from the sun. It fell on prehistoric plants and made them grow. Then as now, green plants were able to do a thing than man cannot yet do—to use the energy of the sun to produce chemical reactions and to build their complicated substance from the carbon dioxide and water of the air plus a few minerals from the soil. It takes energy to do that. It means taking carbon dioxide apart to use the carbon and taking water apart to use the hydrogen and then putting the carbon and hydrogen together again to make cellulose, starch, oils, perfumes and colors. Somehow a substance called chlorophyll, which gives the green color to leaves, is able to do it. Thus it stores the radiant energy of the sun in the materials of the plant. If the leaves or the seeds or even the roots are eaten by animals and man, they are the source of the life energy of the animals. All animals are dependent on plants for their energy since no animal, not even man, is able to store energy direct in edible form. Even the wooden parts of plants are eaten by bacteria, mushrooms, and other plants which are not green and are responsible for what is called decay.

But in ancient times great forests lay where they fell, were not decayed but were buried instead under deposits of mud and sand. Underground pressure and heat transformed the prehistoric logs into coal, still retaining their stored chemical energy. So, also, the remains of ancient sea animals persist as mineral oil or petroleum absorbed in sandstone rocks. Access to the vast deposits of stored chemical energy in coal and petroleum have made the present industrial age possible.

Combustion

The value of having energy stored in solid coal or liquid fuels is that the energy can be released precisely where it is needed—in the furnace at home, in the factory boiler, or within the engine cylinder of an automobile or plane. The energy is chemical; it must be released chemically. The process is familiar, of course. It involves the burning or combustion of the fuel in the oxygen of the atmosphere. To the chemist it involves combination of the hydrogen in the fuel with oxygen to form water and combination of the carbon in the fuel with oxygen to form carbon dioxide. The end products are the same gases —carbon dioxide and water—which some prehistoric plant decomposed with the aid of sunshine aeons ago. And in the combustion the same energy is released that was stored there at that time. Obviously most industrial energy is obtained from combustion of fuels and all combustion involves this chemical combination with oxygen.

The Atom Comes in Here

All this explanation of well-known things is leading up to the explanation of the new atomic energy. It is merely a restatement, in chemical terms, of what everybody knows. Now comes the point where the atom must be brought in because this chemical energy that is released by combustion really comes from the atom too. The point at present is to distinguish between the enormous concentrated energy that has now been tapped (and will be discussed later) and the lesser chemical energy that we have been using all along. Both come from atoms. The new energy comes from the concentrated nucleus at the center of the atom and had better be called nuclear energy. The chemical energy that we get from fuels comes from the surface of the atom. To understand the difference requires taking a look at the atom itself and, for the moment at its surface in order to get at the details of ordinary useful chemical energy:

The idea that matter is composed of small particles which cannot be divided further is at least 2,000 years old. Ancient philosophers, pondering the universe without laboratories or any means of testing their theories, got the notion that any piece of matter can be cut into small bits and these into still smaller ones but that this process cannot go on forever. Ultimately, they supposed, you would get to a particle that is too small to cut further—that has no insides, so to speak. The Latin poet Lucretius in the year 58 B.C. wrote a long poem entitled "On the Nature of Things." Speaking of atoms, he said

> *And these can nor be sundered from without*
> *By beats and blows, nor from within be torn*
> *By penetration, nor be overthrown*
> *By any assault soever through the world . . .*
>
> . . .
>
> *For far beneath the ken of sense lies*
> *The nature of those ultimates of the world;*
> *And so, since those themselves thou canst not see,*
> *Their motion also must they veil from men—*
> *For mark, indeed, how things we can see, oft*
> *Yet hide their motions, when afar from us*
> *Along the distant landscape . . .*

But this was only an idea. To prove it was a bigger job. It was not even attempted until about a hundred years ago. By that time the knowledge of chemical reactions had grown into a major science. The reactions could not be explained except on the theory that there are atoms and that these atoms combine together to form more complex molecules. For instance, there is the fact that one pound of hydrogen requires just eight pounds of oxygen to burn it up and forms exactly nine pounds of water—no more, no less, ever. There is the fact that one pound of carbon requires exactly two and two-thirds pounds of oxygen to form carbon dioxide. Such facts are impossible to explain unless there is an ultimate unit, the hydrogen atom, and a different atom of oxygen, still another of carbon, each of a different weight and with a definite combining power. So for a hundred years chemists have agreed that matter acts as if it were made of atoms. They are ultimate particles of the chemical elements—hydrogen, oxygen, carbon, iron, gold, etc.—which combine in varying numbers to form molecules of the millions of different compounds which compose the earth.

Within the Atom

Until fifty years ago no one gave any thought to the interior of the atom. Almost by definition, the interior was beyond our reach. But radium changed all that. The discovery of radioactivity by Professor Henri Becquerel in Paris and the discovery of radium by a brilliant young Polish student, Maria Sklodowska, who later married her shy, bearded professor, Pierre Curie, struck the scientific world with the same shattering impact that the atomic bomb has now had. Their experiment was quiet enough, but their idea was explosive. It was impossible to understand the rays that were emitted from radium unless they came from inside the radium atom. Ever since 1898 most intensive study has been devoted to the interior of the atom.

It turned out that the radium rays come from deep within the atom in a central kernel, now called the nucleus, which is jampacked with matter and with energy too. It turned out that most of the atom is empty space. Little was actually learned about the nucleus until twenty years later, but it soon appeared that the "surface" of the atom was not a hard shell, as on an egg or a billiard ball, but was merely the orbit of electrons revolving about the nucleus much as the planets revolve about the sun. Without going into details of the proof for this structure of the atom at this point, we need now consider only what the surface electrons mean as the source of chemical energy.

Electronic Energy

It is hardly necessary to explain that electrons are particles of electricity. As long ago as 1910, Dr. Robert A. Millikan, then a young professor at the University of Chicago, proved that electricity too is made of particles, much as matter is made of atoms, but smaller. They are all alike and weigh about 1/2,000th of the weight of the smallest known atom, that of hydrogen. An electric current is merely a stream of electrons which flow through a wire as easily as gas flows through a pipe. They seem to dissolve in metals and can be pumped into any piece of metal by a battery or generator much as a gas can be pumped into a pipe. But the pressure of electrons thus produced is called voltage. The higher the concentration or pressure of electrons in a wire the higher its voltage.

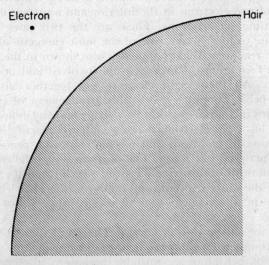

The radius of a human hair is 10,000,000,000 times greater than that of an electron

When a wire is heated they boil out into the air or even into a vacuum surrounding the wire. All these facts concerning electrons are commonplace knowledge in these days of the radio, the telephone, and other electronic industries.

It is not so generally known that the electrons play an essential part in chemical reactions. They do, in all chemical reactions. Only the outermost layer of electrons is involved and these are often known as the chemical electrons. They form the surface of the atom and when two atoms come together the electrons rearrange to form the bond between the atoms and thus make a molecule out of two or more atoms.

In the diagram, the hydrogen atom is represented by a central nucleus and a single electron rotating about it some distance away. This is the simplest of the atoms. The oxygen atom is more complex. It has a nucleus, an orbit of two electrons in the interior and a surface orbit containing six electrons. These are the two gases that combine to form water—one of the most energetic of all known reactions. What happens is also shown in the diagram. Two atoms of hydrogen are involved and one of oxygen. All these eight electrons get together into a single orbit. For some reason this arrangement of eight electrons in a surface orbit is very stable and any molecule which has eight electrons is not a violently reacting one, like those of hydrogen and oxygen, but is a peaceful, stable material like water. The diagram shows the eight-electron orbit of revolving electrons which forms the surface of the water molecule and holds together, by electric forces, the three nuclei—one of oxygen and two of hydrogen.

We are on the trail of energy. The point then is that the incomplete electron orbits in the hydrogen atom and in the oxygen atom are unstable because of the energy in those electrons. When they combine to form a single

HYDROGEN

OXYGEN

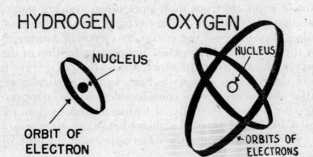

WATER H₂O

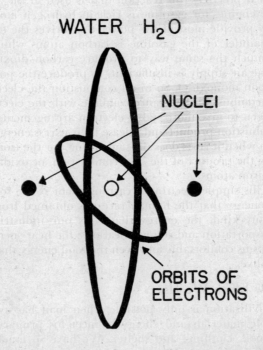

orbit of eight electrons they quiet down and are stable. They have lost energy. As the electrons rearrange in combining they give off the energy as electrical vibrations but these are quickly absorbed and become motion of the water molecule itself. In other words, the energy given off in the reaction appears as heat. In this particular reaction the energy loss is considerable and the temperature rise is great. Actually, if hydrogen and oxygen are mixed and then lighted—i.e., heated—to start the reaction an explosion results and the water appears in the form of steam.

It is precisely this reaction that is used in the automobile engine, for gasoline is rich in hydrogen atoms and they provide most of the power that drives the car. The remainder of the gasoline is carbon atoms which react in much the same way to produce carbon dioxide (or, if the air supply is insufficient, to produce the poisonous carbon monoxide). So in all combustion the electrons of the combustible substance combine with the electrons of oxygen to give more stable electron arrangements in the combustion product and release their excess energy. Even iron when it rusts does the same thing, for the iron rust is only the product of the slow combustion, or oxidation of the iron atoms.

This simple electronic rearrangement is the source of all energy that the human race has obtained from fuels of any kind, the energy that runs our industries, our transportation and communications, the heat energy that keeps us comfortable and even the food energy that keeps us alive.

How Much We Use

Civilization is only possible when man has available ample materials and energy to meet his primary needs of food, clothing, and shelter. We have so much more than the elemental needs in this country that even the worldwide terrors of war give us no conception of what it is to do without them. Yet it has been shown over and over that the moment the economic organization of a people fails to provide these necessities man returns to savagery, to the underlying level of the animal. On the other hand, an economic organization which produces more than enough for the elemental needs immediately permits man to climb to high levels of intellectual and spiritual life. This age is often called materialistic because of the high value we place on materials that are not necessities but luxuries. Yet we are, if anything, more wealthy in energy than we are in materials. We might have called this age energetic rather than materialistic. It is perhaps fortunate that we have not done so, for the new atomic energy is potentially so much greater than all our present energy that there can now be no doubt that the age of energy still lies ahead.

How much energy do we use? For the United States the figure is over a billion horsepower—approximately ten horsepower for every man, woman, and child in the country. And each horsepower is perhaps equal to ten manpower. Thus every American has at his disposal one hundred manpower in machines of various sorts. It is a high standard of living. It is thirty times the figure for China, ten times that for Japan, one and one-half times that for Great Britain and Canada.

The annual production of coal in the world is about 1.2 billion tons. Nearly half of this is United States coal. And in the United States we get about as much energy from petroleum, natural gas, and water power as we get from coal. Our total consumption of energy is about as much as could be gotten from 1.2 billion tons of coal— about three and one-half million tons a day. This is the size of the industry that now looks, wide-eyed and unbelieving, at atomic power.

Power Depends on Speed

One more point needs to be made before we can proceed to look at the nucleus and its tremendous energy. That is the distinction between energy and power. The two words are almost interchangeable in common speech, but to the engineer and the scientist they have quite different meanings. Energy is a quantity—of work done, or of the capacity to do work. Power, on the other hand, is a rate—a rate of doing work or a rate of spending energy. A horse cannot hoist more than a man can but he can hoist it ten times as fast. Given time enough, a ten-horsepower engine can do as much work as a hundred-horsepower engine—but it would take ten times as long to do it. Power, then, is more than energy; it is energy per second or per hour. The factor of speed enters in.

This becomes important when we are dealing with explosives. Gasoline is used in automobiles instead of kerosene not because it contains more energy but because it can give up that energy more rapidly. There is as much energy in a gallon of kerosene as in a gallon of gasoline but one burns slowly, the other is capable of explosion. Chemically, an explosion is a reaction, usually a combustion, which propagates itself through the entire mass of material at high speed. The most powerful explosives are not necessarily those that give the most energy but those that give it quickest. When we discuss atomic power, this will be of the utmost importance.

Explosives

The first modern explosive was gunpowder, a mixture of charcoal, sulfur, and saltpetre. The charcoal and the sulfur, finely powdered, can burn fast and saltpetre provides the oxygen. If the mixture of charcoal and sulfur depended on oxygen from the air for their combustion, they would burn slowly because the reaction would wait for oxygen to seep in. When they are mixed with saltpetre that compound decomposes and delivers the oxygen already intimately mixed with the charcoal and sulfur. Because the oxygen is right on the spot, in the powder itself, the reaction is swift. And if the charge is ignited in a closed space it goes on anyhow, and the hot gaseous products build up enough pressure to explode. In a shotgun the explosion propels the shot towards the game.

But gunpowder is a relatively slow explosive. Modern artillery must send large shells at tremendous velocities and needs explosives that give enormous pressure in the gun in a very small fraction of a second. This was first accomplished by the Swedish chemist, Alfred Nobel, who thereby made a fortune which is now the source of the Nobel Prizes. He managed to get the oxygen for the combustion and the combustible material both into the same molecule. He treated glycerine with nitric acid, got nitroglycerine, the essential constituent of dynamite. It has an unstable molecule in which oxygen is combined with nitrogen from the nitric acid, but not combined with the carbon and hydrogen of the glycerine. On slight provocation the oxygen changes partners, burns the carbon to carbon dioxide, the hydrogen to water—and does so almost instantaneously, with the release of much energy which appears as heat, therefore as pressure. It is a powerful explosive. Even more powerful are guncotton, cordite and TNT (tri-nitro-toluene). They are concentrated energy, and their value lies in the fact that they can release that energy as heat and pressure in a fraction of a second. These and similar explosives have been used on a colossal scale during World War II. They were the last word in explosive power up to June, 1945.

And Now: the Nucleus

All this is preliminary. All this is nineteenth century knowledge which every thinking American should have learned in high school. But chemistry and physics have never been popular subjects in school, have indeed seldom been taught with even a fraction of the interest that the more human subjects have. Teachers and students alike have thought of them as specialties which need only interest the specialist. Those days are over, if indeed they ever existed. It was bad enough for business men, club women, Congressmen, lawyers, and ministers to go through life without any understanding of the tremendous power inherent in science and without any ability to look ahead to its consequences. For decades the world has been changing under our very noses, under the irresistible impact of new scientific discoveries. Most people refuse to look at science, have over and over again been upset by its consequences, yet have merely bewailed the inevitable changes in their lives—or have rushed to buy the newest gadget without a thought as to what it would do to their days, their children, and the structure of our society. Now that the atomic nucleus has erupted into our world with inconceivable energy and power, millions of people everywhere realize that the time has come to understand the basic principles of the science that can be used for so much destruction—and equally well or better for much great good. And it is not possible to understand the atomic bomb without such a quick reminder and survey of those basic principles which are as true now as they were in the nineteenth century. Only a new source of energy has been added, but a big one.

The source is the nucleus of the atom. Up to now our source of energy has been the rearrangement of electrons at the surface of the atom. Now we must look deeper. The atom is empty except for the electrons revolving like planets about a nucleus which would be the sun. This comparison with the solar system cannot be exact, but roughly speaking it is good. The chief difference is that in comparison the nucleus is so small. If we consider the volume of the solar system to be a sphere set on the orbit of Pluto, the outermost planet, and if we consider the volume of the atom to be the sphere set on the orbit of the outermost chemical electrons, then the nucleus at the center of the atom occupies less space in the atom than the sun occupies in the solar system. The size of the nucleus is only one-millionth of a billionth of the size of the atom.

What is it made of? That cannot be simply answered, but one thing is certain: it is not made of anything that we would recognize as matter. Obviously matter is made of atoms, and atoms are mostly empty space. The stuff of which the nucleus is built contains all the actual mass or weight that is in the atom and contains it in a millionth of a billionth of the atom's volume. And so it must be a million billion times as dense as what we call matter. Such stuff is inconceivable.

Concentrated Energy

Furthermore we have long known that the nucleus is also the seat of very concentrated energy. That has been known since the Curies first discovered that a small piece of radium keeps itself several degrees warmer than the air of the room. This was to be expected since the radium rays are absorbed in the materials around it and, like all other spent energy, their energy ultimately becomes heat. But the amount of this heat was astounding. Radium changes very slowly into lead; it takes centuries. But if all the heat emitted by radium throughout its lifetime is added up it amounts to 250,000 times as much energy as is released in burning the same weight of coal.

In those days no one could imagine what that meant but certainly that energy came from the nucleus and so the nucleus must in its tiny compass contain not only matter in incredible concentration but also energy. Investigators were baffled for twenty years in their search for the explanation. It proved impossible to change the rate at which radium gave off its rays. No matter what was done in changing the conditions of temperature, pressure, electricity—radium had its own pace and no one has, even yet, changed it. Later other elements were induced to give rays, and now, fifty years after the discovery of radio-activity, the nucleus has at last been unlocked.

Fifteen years ago the first serious efforts at cracking the nucleus and getting out the energy were begun. The most promising tool was the cyclotron. This is a device to give material particles the highest possible velocity. To smash a nucleus would require a projectile equally small moving at a velocity somewhat comparable to the velocity of light. Indeed only such a small particle as an-other nucleus could be given so high a velocity. The cyclotron does so by using electrical forces. A charged particle, perhaps the nucleus of a hydrogen atom, is whirled by an electrical field and in a spiral path, round and round, increasing its speed at every lap until finally it emerges at top speed and hits a target. Occasionally such a projectile hits a nucleus of the target material and knocks off a chip. Details will be given below. For the present we need note only that cyclotron experiments did show the reality of nuclear energy and the possibility of reaching it. They did not actually ever release any.

The Nucleus Splits

Finally, in 1939, a nucleus was split wide open. It was the most important event of this century—for the present atomic bomb is only one of its consequences. It is worth noting that it took place in the very same city that, later in the same year, saw the next most important event: the declaration of war by Germany on Poland. It was at the Kaiser Wilhelm Institute in Berlin that Professor Otto Hahn and Dr. Lise Meitner learned the trick. The nu-cleus could not be penetrated by an electrically charged particle—presumably because it had to penetrate first the shell of negative electrons in the exterior of the atom and then the shell of positive electricity in the nucleus.

But a neutral (not electrically charged) particle can not be accelerated in a cyclotron. So a high-speed neutral particle was obtained by the bombardment of the light metal, beryllium, with alpha rays such as come from radium. Such a neutral projectile can penetrate the nucleus and did so under the clever hands of Dr. Hahn and Miss Meitner.

They used uranium as the target. Uranium has the largest atom of any of the known elements. It would seem to be the most likely to crack if any nucleus could crack, just because no larger atoms are known. It is just possible that any larger atoms would break up of their own accord—in fact would have broken up long ago and so do not exist. Whatever the reason, the uranium atom did break up into two smaller atoms. But the weight of the two fragments did not quite add up to the weight of the original atom. Some six percent of the mass had disappeared. It had been transformed into energy, as Einstein had predicted nearly thirty years earlier.

The breaking of a nucleus into two smaller ones was triumph enough but the release of energy exceeded all expectations. The fragments of the nucleus were hurled off with an energy of 100,000,000 electron volts. This is far beyond any energy previously known on earth. The previous record was the energy imparted to a very tiny charged nucleus in the cyclotron, and that was only 32,-000,000 volts. The violent explosion of some of the radioactive elements related to radium produces 14,000,000 electron volts. But the uranium atom cracked apart by Hahn and Meitner gave 100,000,000.

That was in 1939. It had been done. But it had been done with single atoms one by one. There was nothing practical about it. A single nucleus, even when hurled

at 100,000,000 electron volts, is still a very tiny quantity
of energy. Because, of course, the atom is so small. In the
pictorial language of the schoolroom an atom is so small
that if a drop of water were magnified to the size of the
earth the atoms in it would hardly be the size of oranges.
So, to practical people, the Hahn and Meitner splitting
of the uranium nucleus was of no particular interest.

But to scientists the world over that was the day when
the atomic age dawned. If that was the dawn, then sunrise came in New Mexico on June 16, 1945, when the first
real test of an atomic bomb was made. In science a period
of five years between dawn and sunrise is phenomenally
short. Except for those actually on the project, no one
expected results for another twenty years, perhaps fifty.
But there was reason for hurry. The war had to be won.
If we did not hurry, the enemy would. And so we spent
two billion dollars, built three cities, spared neither time
nor money nor men so that Hiroshima could be the large-
scale test and proof on August 6, 1945. The atomic age
had opened.

The Clues to the Puzzle

VERY FEW DISCOVERIES in the long history of mankind
rank with the solution of the problem of atomic power.
Many of the greatest were accidents and in most cases
the discoverers hardly knew what they had accomplished.
The invention of fire, the discovery of America, the discovery of oxygen in the casual experiments of an English
clergyman, the discovery of X-rays by Wilhelm Roentgen,
were all incidents or accidents. But atomic power was the
goal of one of the longest and most difficult series of researches in history. Faint hints were picked up here and
there throughout the years by individual workers in many
lands. Gradually the conviction grew that the atom has a
nucleus, that the nucleus contains colossal energy, that
the nucleus can be unlocked to give up that energy.

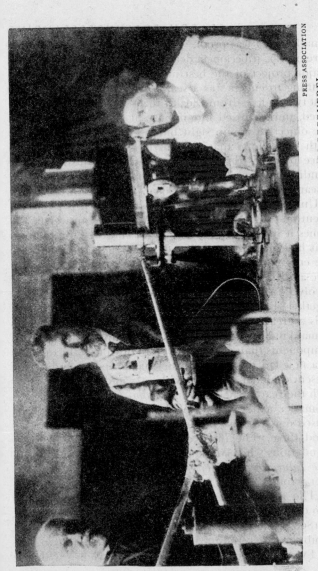

PIERRE and MARIE CURIE. The man on the left is probably HENRI BECQUEREL

Finally there was proof. Then suddenly, under the pressure of war, it became a determined and highly organized major project of the best minds in the world. From beginning to end it was a search covering fifty years. The first twenty-five—from 1895 to 1920—were the years of scattered, unrecognized but important clues. From then on the objective was in sight but twenty more years passed with little hope that the puzzle could be solved. Only since 1940 was there enough assurance to justify the expenditure of two billion dollars on the most determined research project ever undertaken.

Unique as the story is in these respects, it is typical of scientific progress in one thing. When the answer finally comes it bursts on the front pages and over the radio as if it had all happened that day. Few people understand the enormous complexity of the work that has gone before and the number of individual researchers that were involved in finding the separate clues and in piecing them together. Fewer care. But this atomic bomb is different. It is a greater achievement in terms of its consequences to mankind than any previous one. It involves more great components than any other. It is so obviously the opening of a new era that one quipster has proposed ending the present calendar sequence with 1945 and beginning anew with the year 1 A.A., for *Anno Atomi*.

Smaller achievements, incidental to this great one, have caused similar consternation among those few who understood them. The intellectual world was shocked to its foundations when Madame Curie discovered radium. In *The Education of Henry Adams*, that urbane philosopher wrote:

"The man of science must have been sleepy indeed who did not jump from his chair like a scared dog when, in 1898, Mme Curie threw on his desk the metaphysical bomb she called radium. There remained no hole to hide in. Even metaphysics swept back over science with the green water of the deep-sea ocean and no one could longer hope to bar out the unknowable, for the unknowable was known."

Radium was a metaphysical bomb. Nuclear power is, in awful truth, a real bomb, as shattering as any thousand previous bombs. This time it is not only the man of science who jumps like a scared dog but the man on the street and the woman at home who jumps—and rightly. Now that the first shock is over, now that every citizen must face this awesome power and decide what to do with it, it is time to take thought and review the events that led up to what may be the greatest catastrophe the human race has ever known but should be a blessed godsend. It is a story of hard work, brilliant hunches, keen thinking.

The Discovery of Radium

The modern era began with the discovery of X-rays, followed immediately by the discovery of radioactivity. In *Matter and Energy*, by Wendt and Smith, published by The Blakiston Company, the essential facts are covered:

"Professor Roentgen of the University of Munich had hardly made his astonishing accidental discovery of X-rays, in 1895, when Professor Becquerel of the University of Paris, by an equally fortunate accident discovered that compounds of the metal uranium appear to give off these rays naturally and continuously. When this was followed by the discovery of radium by Professor and Madame Curie at Paris in 1898, the scientific world was shaken to its foundations. X-rays were not yet understood; the electron was unknown. There were forces at work in these new discoveries which were beyond the range of human imagination at the time. It was thrilling enough to produce a radiation that could pass through solid opaque objects. It was incomprehensible to find a natural substance which without the application of energy of any sort gives out those same rays in huge quantities and without appearing to suffer any loss. It seemed to be a violation of the principle that energy cannot be created. It was a shocking realization that, after all, we know very little about this world in which we live. . . .

"Radium and several other rare elements that are related to it differ from other elements in that they are constantly pouring forth energy in various forms. Professor Becquerel found that any material containing uranium will leave its record on a photographic plate in complete darkness, and even when the plate is wrapped in a heavy sheet of black paper these materials give out rays that affect the photographic plate just as light does. The Curies investigated a large number of materials, especially the ores of uranium and thus found a new element, radium, which is always associated with uranium ores, and which is a million times as active as uranium in its action on the photographic plate—in the property which became known as radioactivity. They found that radium is in other respects a typical metal, very similar to calcium and barium. It forms the whole range of compounds that any metal forms. They discovered, however, that the rays are emitted by the radium atoms at a definite rate irrespective of the molecule which contains the atom and also without being influenced by physical conditions. The rays are emitted at a definite rate which is the same for all samples of radium no matter what the temperature or the magnetic, electrical or other conditions of energy. They found that this emission of radioactive energy is enormous in quantity. All radium-containing substances keep themselves at a temperature higher than their surroundings. A gram of radium spontaneously gives off enough energy to melt one gram of ice each minute and this energy comes from within the atom itself. Furthermore, these materials are

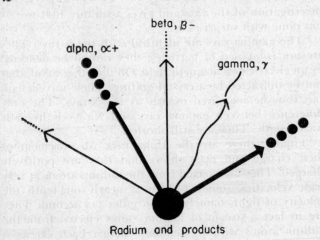

Radium and products

luminous. Any radium compound can be seen by its own light, though this light is faint and is visible only in a dark room. There is only a very slow diminution in the rate of energy emission, such that the rate would be cut in half in about 2,000 years. These phenomena are sufficiently astonishing to justify a complete revision of the conceptions of matter and energy which were prevalent at the time of their discovery.

"It was soon found that the emission of light and of heat, surprising as they were, were only secondary effects and that the primary action ·was the emission of three other types of rays which go under the names of alpha, beta, and gamma rays. The beta rays turn out to be electrons, identical in every respect with the electrons found in other rays. The electrons from some radioactive substances, however, move with a velocity which indicates an electrical potential of as much as five million volts. It appears that such enormous electrical potentials exist within the radium atom. This is the first fruit of the investigation of the rays and gives assurance that we are not done with surprises.

"The gamma rays are identical with the X-rays. They are not composed of particles; they cannot be deflected by an electric or a magnetic field. On the other hand, they can be diffracted by a crystal grating. Their wave-length can thus be measured exactly as for X-rays. The only difference between gamma rays and X-rays is in their wave-length. They are still shorter. . . .

"Finally, there are the alpha rays. Measurement of their charge and mass shows that they are positively charged. They are ejected from the radium atoms at very high velocities, some of them at nearly one-tenth the velocity of light, namely 20,000 miles per second. They are in fact a stream of helium atoms ejected from the radium atoms with tremendous energy. Each carries a double charge of positive electricity—in other words, each atom is missing two electrons. For some reason, then, the radium atoms eject helium atoms which lack two electrons and these constitute the alpha rays.

"Obviously such things cannot go on without having a serious effect on the radium atom itself. This atom weighs 226 units of atomic weight. It ejects a helium atom weighing 4 units. It ejects electrons with velocities almost equal to that of light. It is set into violent vibration, thus giving very high-frequency gamma rays. All this energy must come from somewhere and the radium atom must undergo tremendous transformation in the process. We can hardly be surprised if what remains after all this explosive energy is released is no longer recognizable as a radium atom.

"Such is the case. Further study by Madame Curie and her students after the death of her revered husband showed that radium changes into a gas called radon and this into other elements all of which give off rays and disintegrate further until the end product of the whole series is lead. By that time the original radium has lost a large proportion of its weight, reduced from 226 units to 206. Furthermore, radium itself was found to be formed by the disintegration of the heaviest of all the elements, uranium, the weight of which is 238 units. . . .

"We are thus here dealing with a series of atoms which are unstable, which break up of their own accord, thereby emitting either alpha or beta rays and forming a new and lighter atom. This raises a host of interesting questions. The first is, of course, what causes the explosions. This no one has answered. We have already seen that the rate at which these rays are emitted depends only on the number of atoms present. No means have ever been found for changing this rate in the slightest degree. Let us note, however, that any one atom of radium can explode only once and having done so becomes an atom of radon. In the aggregate, however, the rate at which these explosions take place is such that every two thousand years the quantity of radium remaining is cut in half. The same situation holds with regard to radon but here it is more easily studied because any quantity of radon will be reduced to one-half in just 3.86 days. If we start with one gram today, we shall have only half a gram in a little less than four days; four days after that we shall have only a quarter of a gram, and still four days later only an eighth. This means that a certain definite fraction of all the atoms present will explode during any given time. In this present second, for instance, a certain small fraction is exploding and forming a new element. The others are unchanged. If we could segregate them from those which do explode, we should never suppose that they were any different from ordinary atoms. They will behave in every way like the normal atoms of a metal in the case of radium and of a gas in the case of radon. We have, however, no way of telling in advance which atoms are going to explode. The atoms themselves cannot know or anticipate the explosion. The simple fact is that a certain small proportion are bound to explode every second. We do not know what causes it but there is a sublime fatalism in the fact that some of them are bound to explode within the next second while others may continue in their present state for centuries. The explosion seems to be an accident and yet one that is bound to happen to a definite number of atoms each second. We cannot even guess why certain of the atoms are chosen and others are given a longer life. We face again one of nature's mysteries which is the more shocking because its action is so definite and inexorable.

"In addition, we can but speculate as to what sort of thing the radioactive atom is. In other respects it is just like other atoms, inconceivably minute, unaffected by anything that man can do with it, and apparently an ultimate constituent of matter. If it were not for radioactivity we should still suppose that the atom is the final stage in the possible subdivision of things.

"But radium proves that the atom must be complex. Within its tiny sphere there are forces beyond human understanding. Electrons are ejected with velocities that point to the existence of electric fields of potentials as high as five million volts per centimeter. Explosions take place such that a fraction of the material atom is ejected at a tremendous velocity. Certainly this atom cannot be ultimate. It contains both electrons and atoms of helium. For some reason these helium fragments are emitted in successive explosions so that going from uranium, atomic weight 238, to lead, atomic weight 206, no less than eight successive helium atoms are sent forth. Far from being an ultimate and indivisible particle, the atom is here revealed as being complex and the seat of much concentrated energy. We have solved many problems by discovering the atom and we have made the picture definite by the study of alpha, beta, and gamma rays, but the ultimate mystery has only receded and become more impressive. To go on we must explore the interior of the atom."

Within the Atom

The next set of clues in the long hunt came from England where the gifted New Zealander, Ernest Rutherford, had become director of the Cavendish Laboratory at Cambridge. He and his students pushed the frontiers of knowledge deep into the atom and answered many questions that Madame Curie had raised. He became Sir Ernest and finally Lord Rutherford. It was he who shot alpha particles from radium into thin foils of metal, measured the number that went through and the number that were deflected back towards their source in spite of their terrific energy. It was painful and detailed work but he emerged with the conclusion that most of these atomic projectiles went clean through the thin, though solid, wall of metal as if it were not there, while those that were reflected must have met a small but very dense obstacle in the metallic atoms of the foil. The only explanation was that the atoms comprising the metal foil were mostly

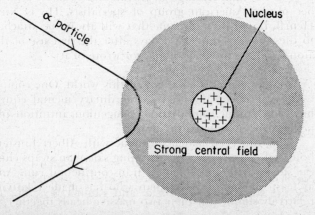

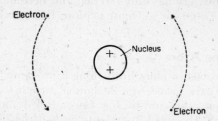

empty so that these tiny projectiles could sail through without resistance. But at the center of the metallic atoms, he said, there must be a very small but very dense nucleus. He estimated that the diameter of the atom was a hundred thousand times the diameter of the nucleus. If this were so the volume of the atom would be a million billion times the volume of the nucleus. Thus, if the nucleus were magnified to the size of a small nut then the diameter of the atom would be almost a mile. Yet all the matter of the atom would be in the nucleus.

Next in the line of development of these clues comes the name of a man who is still active and played a major part in the final triumph of the atomic bomb as a member of the American group of specialists. He is Niels Henrik David Bohr, a name that will always be attached to the nuclear atom. Two days after the first use of the atomic bomb, the *New York Sun* wrote of it:

"He has a mind that is out of this world. One competent critic once said, 'His extraordinary mental equipment is a unique combination of ingenious intuition and penetrating mathematical power.'

"Bohr can even match formulae with Albert Einstein hours on end the way one traveling salesman swaps clubcar stories with another on a transcontinental run. And at least once he and the man who has made relativity relatively simple put their two massive heads together.

"The idea was to work out something no one or several minds had ever before been able to fathom. The result was the last you would expect from such a collaboration. It was nothing. The pair of them didn't get to first base.

"Bohr, either with or without Einstein's aid has, of course, got well past Relativity's first base. To him its more than Eleusinian mysteries are as plain as a picket fence. Moreover he holds out hope for the rest of us. The whole of mankind, he is sure, will one day get the entire hang of it.

"He is a fellow whose assurance can be depended on. He is a very dependable fellow. Twenty years and more ago the Rockefeller International Educational Board con-

URANIUM ATOM

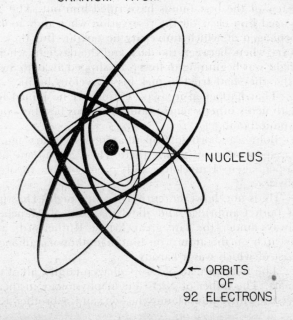

NUCLEUS

← ORBITS
OF
92 ELECTRONS

sidered him so dependable that it handed him $40,000 for research. He didn't disappoint, either.

"The research, of course, concerned the same atom which Bohr has now helped crack or control or whatever, to the Japs' misery. He has been for a long while one of the world's great atomic authorities and was famous before he was thirty.

"Columbia University, before Bohr reached forty, was glad to have him over for a course of lectures, and universities and scientific tongs everywhere have been proud to whisper their passwords. In all the great capitals and a lot of whistle stops he could spread his coat tails among the most select savants and receive the grip of membership.

"At any rate he could before the war. Since then quite a few of the best bunds have ruled him out. The Nazis fenced him clear off the reservation when they took Copenhagen at which university he taught. But they were sorry when, between the dark and the daylight when the night was beginning to lower, he slipped away to Sweden after they had tried to pick his marvelous brain.

"That happened in 1943. Ultimately he joined forces with many other scientists and put in his best licks on the atomic bomb.

"Bohr was born in Copenhagen, sixty years ago, and has spent most of his life there. He is a graduate of the Copenhagen University and professor of theoretical physics.

"He is not, however, entirely home taught. He studied at both Cambridge and the University of Manchester, always under the late great Ernest Rutherford, whose research on the atom won him many honors, among the least of which was a barony.

"The Bohrs are an old Copenhagen family, all of them smart. The father of Niels taught physiology in the university which now claims the son, and a brother is one

PROFESSOR HAROLD C. UREY

DR. NIELS BOHR

of the world's great mathematicians. Married since 1912, the atomic Bohr has four sons.

"He is big and solid, with a strong, creased face overhung by the remnants of a once thick shock of hair. He speaks slowly through broad lips, and his platform manner is quiet. As often as not he stands with his hands shoved into his coat pockets. As often as not the coat could could stand a pressing.

"Sometimes he is on a platform a long while without clearing up very much. Once he talked for two hours to Toronto's sharpest citizens none of whom, later, would admit he had understood a word the wise doctor had said.

"But he is really wise. That ultimate commendation, the Nobel Prize, was awarded him twenty-three years ago."

As far back as 1913, when Niels Bohr was a student with Sir Ernest Rutherford at Cambridge University and Sir Ernest had just proposed his nuclear theory, Bohr produced some evidence that set that theory on its feet. He showed that the light that comes from atoms when they are heated, light that can be analyzed by the spectroscope, agrees nicely with Rutherford's theory. The Bohr theory and the encouragement it gave to the first efforts at atom-smashing is described by James Stokley in *Science Remakes Our World* (published by Ives Washburn) as follows:

"We can illustrate Bohr's concept with the simplest atom, that of hydrogen. There is a nucleus, consisting of a unit charge of positive electricity, and revolving around this a negative unit charge, or an electron. Normally, the electron moves in an elliptical orbit around the nucleus, like a planet around the sun. However, there are other possible orbits, farther out from the nucleus, in which the electron can be made to move when energy is applied to it. But then it tends spontaneously to return to its favorite orbit, and as it does so it gives out the energy again as a burst of radiation, or light either visible or invisible. There are a number of possible jumps that the electron may make, and each shows a characteristic note, or wavelength. Other atoms are more complicated, with more electrons and more orbits, so they have more possible jumps, and more lines in their spectrum, in many cases.

"Nowadays physicists no longer picture the electrons as little planets revolving around in nice, precise orbits. Rather have the orbits themselves become rather hazy regions in which, probably, the electron will be found, while the electron is not a definite entity either, but a sort of waviness.

"However, the atom has been shown to be a complicated thing. We might compare it with a watch, a complex assemblage of mechanism surrounded by a metal case. The atom does not have the metal case, but it does have a shell, made up by the field of force which surrounds it. Ordinary chemistry does not penetrate this shell, but our new chemistry does—it gets into the heart, or nucleus, of the atom.

Penetration Bullets

"The physicists' most powerful artillery was needed to get through the shell, and reach the nucleus. 'Artillery' is used advisedly, for the process actually consists of firing bullets at the atom; not ordinary bullets, but bullets which are pieces of atoms themselves, of a size comparable with the atoms to be smashed. The first to be used were those constantly given off by radium; nuclei of helium atoms, also called 'alpha particles.' These have energies high enough to penetrate the forces around the nucleus, provided you aim them right.

"Since you cannot see either the atoms you are trying

to hit or the bullets with which you are shooting, aiming is out of the question. But if you are in a dark cellar in which a swarm of bats is flying, and you have a machine gun which you spray around, you will occasionally hit a bat. This is in effect what Sir Ernest Rutherford did at Cambridge University in 1919, when he accomplished the first actual transmutation of one element into another and realized the alchemist's dream.

"His apparatus was a box containing nitrogen gas. Inside was a bit of radium, the machine gun, while the nitrogen atoms were the bats. At one end of the box was a 'window' of thin silver. Outside this window was a screen of zinc sulfide, a material which glows with momentary starlike points of light every time an alpha particle strikes. But no particles struck it, for the silver window was just too thick to let them pass.

"Occasionally a spark of light did appear on the screen! Here was a particle that came from the box with more energy than an alpha particle. Rutherford studied these new particles in various ways—by measuring the effect on them, for example, of a magnet—and established that they were nuclei of hydrogen atoms, or what soon came to be called protons. What had happened was that an alpha particle had squarely hit the nucleus of a nitrogen atom, and had, indeed, been captured by it. A proton had been given off. But the alpha particle itself consists of two charges—two protons. Hence the nitrogen nucleus had one more proton than before—it had eight instead of the seven which it normally carried. However, the element with eight protons in the nucleus is not nitrogen —it is oxygen! Not ordinary oxygen, but a form in which the nucleus is one unit heavier than the ordinary kind.

Isotopes

"Most of the elements have been found to exist in these several different weights, and the separate forms are called 'isotopes.' Ordinary oxygen, which makes up a fifth of the air, contains 99.76 per cent of an isotope of weight 16, a very small amount of weight 17 (the kind that Rutherford produced) and a fifth of a per cent of weight 18 as well. But the transmuted nucleus of heavy oxygen contained not only one more proton than the nitrogen nucleus from which it was produced: the alpha particle also left two neutrons. These are particles that another Cambridge scientist, James Chadwick, had discovered in 1932. With the same mass as the proton, but having no electrical charge, the neutron fitted very conveniently into concepts of atomic changes.

"It explained, for example, why two isotopes can have different weights yet be the same element. The number of protons in the nucleus (the same as the number of electrons in an element in its normal state) determines what the element is. Thus, all nitrogen atoms have seven protons, and all oxygen atoms have eight. Ordinary oxygen has in addition eight neutrons, but its heavy isotopes have either nine (for weight 17) or (to make weight 18) ten.

"There is also a heavy form of hydrogen, called 'deuterium,' which Dr. Harold C. Urey of Columbia University discovered in 1932. Ordinary hydrogen contains it in the proportion of about one part in five thousand, but it can be separated into a nearly pure state. Its nuclei, celled 'deuterons,' have proved the most effective atom-smashing bullets thus far.

"A deuteron consists of a proton, like the nucleus of ordinary hydrogen, plus a neutron, making it twice as heavy. Because it has a single charge, it is just as easily fired by electrical forces at the nucleus as is the solitary proton. And when it gets close to the nucleus of the atom under attack, the neutron is released to perform its mission. However, neutrons by themselves, and also protons, unaccompanied, are used as atomic bullets as well.

"Protons were the projectiles which Cockroft and Walton used in 1932, speeding them up with energy equivalent to 700,000 volts and aiming them at lithium. Nuclei of helium atoms—alpha particles—were given off. This was actually the first success at atom-smashing with laboratory apparatus, since the alpha particles that Rutherford had used were produced by natural processes taking place in the radium, and not under the control of man.

The Cyclotron

"To advance further required the use of more energetic particles. Higher voltages were needed to send the bullets on their way. Two machines have been used to do this. One is the Van de Graaff generator. Essentially, this generates electricity in the same way you may generate it on a winter day, when you scuff your feet on a rug and draw a spark from a light fixture or some unsuspecting person's ear. In rubbing over the rug, you accumulate an electrical charge. The central part of the Van de Graaff machine is an endless belt of insulating material on to which an electrical charge is sprayed. The upper end of the belt is inside a hollow metal sphere, and its motion carries the charges to this sphere. There they are drawn off; the sphere itself accumulates the charge, while the belt goes down again for more. When the charge is great enough, it can overcome the natural resistance of the air; and a spark jumps to near-by grounded metal. By enclosing the entire apparatus in a tank, with gas under pressure, the resistance is increased and higher voltages—up to 5,000,000 volts—may be obtained. Then these voltages may be used to accelerate positive or negative particles for atom-smashing experiments. Several of these Van de Graaff generators have been installed in great research laboratories.

"The other and even more popular atom-smashing weapon is the cyclotron, invention of Dr. Ernest O. Law-

Views of Notre Dame atom smasher

rence of the University of California. It reaches higher voltages, but they cannot be as accurately controlled. We can think of it as a sort of atomic sling-shot—the kind that David used to slay Goliath, when he whirled a stone around his head in a sling, then let it fly when it had gained sufficient speed.

". . . Dr. W. D. Coolidge cascaded electrons to speed them to high energies. By applying voltages of perhaps one hundred thousand several times in successive steps, the particles were given successive boosts and attained energies equaling the sum of these steps. With a device called the linear accelerator the same thing can be done with protons, and this device has been widely used in atom-smashing experiments. In fact, in 1931 Lawrence himself, then thirty years of age, speeded particles to a million and a quarter volts.

"But the linear accelerator gets longer and longer as its power is increased, and this imposes a limit beyond which it is too unwieldy to use.

"Then Lawrence turned to the sling-shot idea. The cyclotron was the result, winning for him the Nobel Prize in Physics in 1939, the last given. Electrons from a hot filament hit molecules of a gas, such as hydrogen; and protons (or deuterons if the gas is heavy hydrogen) are formed inside a chamber that is well evacuated, for very little gas is needed to supply the bullets. Also in this vacuum chamber are two hollow D-shaped electrodes,

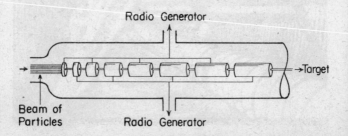

Radio Generator

Beam of Particles

Radio Generator

→Target

called "dees." Cut a pill box into two semicircular halves, separate the halves slightly, and you have a good model of these dees.

"The dees are connected to, essentially, a powerful short-wave radio transmitter, giving a rapidly oscillating electrical current. Each dee is continually changing from negative to positive, then back again, many times per second, and the two dees are always oppositely charged. Our proton, then, knocked out of a hydrogen atom by an electron, has a positive charge; it is attracted to the negative dee. Since the entire vacuum chamber is between the poles of a powerful magnet, the magnetic field causes the proton to move in a semicircle, back to the opening between the dees. By this time their charges are reversed; now the other has the negative charge, so the proton is yanked across the opening with an increase in speed.

"Again it moves in a semicircle, under the magnetic influence; again it comes to the gap, again the field has changed. Now the first dee is again negative, so the proton has another jerk. It goes around and around, moving in ever-widening circles accelerating each time it crosses

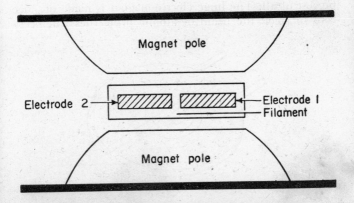

the space between the dees. Compared with the linear accelerator, the voltage used in any one jump is small; in some of Lawrence's early experiments it was only about four thousand.

"Finally our proton is traveling around the edge of one dee, then it comes within reach of a negatively charged plate which pulls it out of the dees entirely. It passes easily through a thin metal window, out into the open air where it can be used to bombard anything that happens to be in range. What happens to one proton (or deuteron) is, of course, happening to a swarm, and they all emerge as a potent beam.

"The first cyclotron was only four inches in diameter, and a small magnet sufficed. But to increase the power, bigger and bigger magnets had to be used. At the University of California's Radiation Laboratory in Berkeley, of which Lawrence is director, a sixty-inch machine, with a 220-ton magnet, speeds the particles to energies of around 16,000,000 volts. More than thirty other cyclotrons are in regular use in research laboratories throughout the world; and Lawrence and his colleagues have in an advanced state of construction, on a Berkeley hill overlooking San Francisco Bay and the Golden Gate, the biggest of all. The huge electro-magnet is made of 4,900 tons of steel; the beam of atomic projectiles will be so

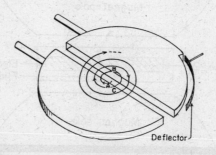

Deflector

powerful that it will penetrate, it is expected, about 140 feet of air. The voltage will be between 100 and 300 million.

"When this cyclotron goes into operation many now formidable barriers to science's insight into the atom will undoubtedly be broken down. As the protons, deuterons, or even nuclei of helium atoms are spun around, some of them stray from the main beam, hit the copper walls of the chamber, knock neutrons out of the copper atoms, to be strewn around promiscuously. A cyclotron therefore is usually surrounded by tanks of water several feet thick, which form barriers to the wandering neutrons.

"But often neutrons are desired for use in experiments. Then they are produced by bombarding lithium, beryllium, or some similar light metal with the deuterons. It was in this way, for example, that two Harvard University physicists, according to their report in 1941 to the American Physical Society, realized the dream of the alchemists; for mercury was turned into gold. The physicists are Dr. Rubby Sherr and Dr. Kenneth T. Bainbridge. No vast fortunes awaited them as a result, however, for the amounts of gold produced were so insignificant that an indirect means of detecting it had to be resorted to. Also, the gold was in the form of isotopes which quickly decayed into other elements, some in a few minutes, others in several days.

"The method Sherr and Bainbridge used shows some of the ingenious tricks that science must employ in these researches. Deuterons from the Harvard cyclotron were fired at lithium, neutrons were obtained and, in turn, used to bombard mercury. Then a small bit of gold was mixed with the mercury and the mercury was boiled away, leaving the gold by itself again, except for minute amounts of platinum, which had also been formed by transmutation from the mercury. This was removed by a chemical process. When the gold was tested, it was found that it contained several new forms which behaved like radium, spontaneously disintegrating and giving off certain kinds of radiation in the process.

Artificial Radioactivity

"It is in making radioactive elements artificially, however, that the cyclotron has had one of its most important applications. In fact, some have been erected with this main purpose rather than for use primarily in research into the atomic nucleus. Radium, and all the substances like it, that we call 'radioactive,' show a characteristic distintegration into other elements, with the liberation of one of three types of ray as they do so. In the case of radium the disintegration proceeds at such a rate that, after 1690 years, half of the original amount will be gone; at the end of another 1690 years, half of that will have disintegrated, and so on. This 1690-year period is said to be the 'half-life' of radium. Some radioactive substances have much longer half-lives, while others, including most of those made artificially, are much shorter, some being measured in small fractions of a second.

"Radioactive phosphorus, which is made when you expose ordinary phosphorus to the beam of a cyclotron, has a half-life of fourteen days, which is a very convenient length of time. It can be injected into the body, where it performs its mission; yet after that its activity dies away. If you were to inject radium into the body, it would keep up its activity long after it was needed for therapy, and would then do considerable harm. These radioactive elements behave chemically just like the same elements in the customary form, and in the body they behave the same way too. The phosphorus is deposited in the bones, and that makes the radioactive form effective for treating leukemia, a disease in which the white blood cells,

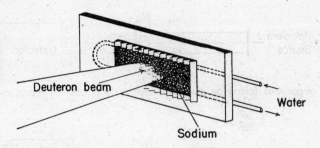

Deuteron beam

Water

Sodium

Sodium becomes radioactive when bombarded by
deuterons from the cyclotron

necessary in moderate amounts for combating infection,
run away and overproduce. These cells originate in the
bone marrow, so, when the radioactive phosphorus is
deposited in the bones, it is just where it is needed for
the greatest effect.

"Another important use of artificially radioactive elements is as 'tracers.' Botanists, for example, have found
them useful in studying the physiology of plants. Suppose
that you want to trace the path of phosphorus through
a plant's anatomy. Phosphorus goes in at one place, and
is later found elsewhere; but how can you be sure that
these are the same atoms? By making them radioactive,
the atoms can be tagged. That is, radioactive phosphorus
is formed, and mixed with the plant's nutriment. As the
radioactive atoms reach various leaves, for example, they
can be detected. The beta rays, really electrons, which
they give off, will write their autograph on a photographic plate. Or another form of detector, called the
Geiger counter, will reveal their presence by flashes of
an electric lamp connected to it, or by clicks in a loud
speaker. Similarly, radioactive tracers can be fed to animals, in studying the operation of their bodies.

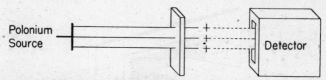

∝ particles falling on aluminum screen cause positron emission.

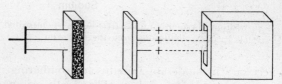

Lead shield blocks ∝ particles; positron emission continues.

"Radioactivity can be induced in other ways than with the cyclotron. In fact, it was first accomplished with a natural source, and there is a most appropriate family connection here. Madame Marie Curie, and her husband, Pierre, discovered radium in 1898. It was in 1933 that their daughter Irene and her husband, Frederick Joliot, discovered artificial radioactivity; and they used the rays from polonium (one of the other radium elements which Marie Curie had also discovered) to provide the rays. When they employed alpha rays from polonium to bombard a piece of aluminum, it gave off other rays which proved to be positrons—particles like the electron, but carrying a positive charge. Even after the bombardment was terminated, the aluminum continued its radiation, and this gradually weakened, in the same manner as the rays from natural radium gradually weaken.

"Then Enrico Fermi, an Italian physicist who is now at Columbia University, one of the galaxy of brilliant

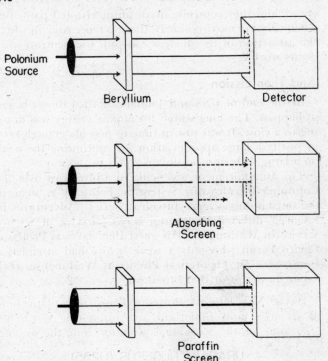

Polonium Source

Beryllium

Detector

Absorbing Screen

Paraffin Screen

scientists that America has secured as a result of Axis shortsightedness, showed the effect of slow neutrons. He made neutrons by shooting alpha particles at beryllium powder; but these directly did not have an effect. However, when he passed his neutrons through a substance such as paraffin and reduced their speed, they became much more effective. This seems contradictory, but it has a reasonable explanation. When the bullets tear past the atomic nucleus at full speed, they are there such a short time that they have little opportunity to be influenced, and they continue in an uninterrupted path. But when they are moving slowly, there is more time in which the attraction of the nucleus can pull the neutron in to do its work."

And Then Fission

By the end of 1938 and January of 1939 things began to happen. The long search for atomic energy was drawing to a close. It was just in time to provide enough facts to justify a large appropriation for continuing the work on a large scale as a possible weapon in the war.

The announcement was made in a broadcast over the Columbia Broadcasting System on February 2, 1939, in the outstanding science broadcast series "Adventures in Science," directed by Watson Davis, director of Science Service in Washington. His guest that day was Professor Enrico Fermi who only a week before had attended a Conference on Theoretical Physics at Washington, D.C. From the script of that broadcast:

DAVIS: Now let's ask Professor Fermi to explain some of science's most important and interesting researches . . . some of the work that won for him the famous

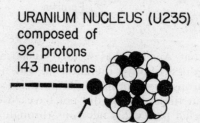

URANIUM NUCLEUS (U235)
composed of
92 protons
143 neutrons

One isolated neutron shot into nucleus explodes the atom and releases tremendous energy in the nucleus.

Neutrons from exploded atom bombard other uranium atoms
and explode them.

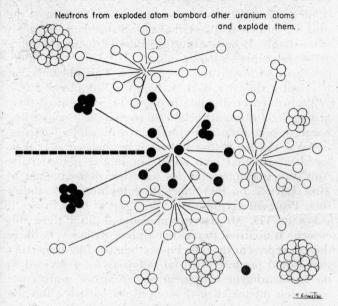

M. Bramilku

Nobel Prize. . . . Professor Fermi, when did modern
atomic transmutation really begin?

FERMI: Although the problem of transmuting elements
into each other is much older than a satisfactory definition of the very concept of what is a chemical element,
the first and most important step towards its solution
was made by the late Lord Rutherford. It was only in
1919 that he pioneered the method of nuclear bombard-
ments. He showed that when the nucleus of a light element is struck by a fast-moving alpha particle, it is
transformed into the nucleus of a different kind of atom.

DAVIS: You might say that Lord Rutherford blasted
H out of matter, the H in this case standing for hydrogen.

FERMI: The new atomic nucleus, or heart, formed by
the bombardment, may be the same as one of the known

stable nuclei. But this is not necessarily so. Sometimes the nucleus formed is different from all ordinary nuclei. It is not stable. It behaves instead like the naturally radioactive substances, such as radium. It disintegrates spontaneously with emission of electrons. This phenomenon is called artificial radioactivity. Joliot and Irene Curie of Paris discovered it late in 1933. They produced their first three kinds of artificial radioactivity by bombarding boron, magnesium, and aluminum with alpha particles.

DAVIS: All the textbooks had to be changed after that, for they said that man could not induce radioactivity. And Professor Joliot and his wife, who is a daughter of Mme Curie, won the Nobel Prize for this work, didn't they, Professor Fermi?

FERMI: Yes, Mr. Davis. Immediately after these discoveries it occurred to me that alpha particles very likely did not represent the only type of bombarding projectiles that would produce artificial radioactivity. I decided to try bombardment with neutrons. Neutron sources are much less intense than those of alpha particles. But the fact that neutrons have no electric charge makes it easier for them to reach the nucleus of the bombarded substance. They do not have to overcome the repulsion of the electric field that surrounds the atomic nucleus.

DAVIS: What did you find, Professor Fermi?

FERMI: Beginning with the very first experiments, I proved that most of the elements tested—37 out of 63—became radioactive under the effect of the neutron bombardment. My collaborators and I in the physical laboratory of the University of Rome carried out a systematic investigation of the behavior of a large number of chemical elements. In most cases we succeeded in identifying and separating by chemical analysis the newly formed radioactive atoms. This identification permitted us to guess just how and by what steps a nucleus changed to give a new radioactive element.

DAVIS: You even succeeded in affecting the heaviest of all elements, thorium and uranium, didn't you, Professor Fermi?

FERMI: Yes, neutrons can reach all nuclei, whereas the alpha particles do not have energy enough to overcome the strong electrical repulsion of the heavy nuclei.

DAVIS: And as a result there was found evidence that there can be produced new chemical elements heavier than hitherto thought possible, elements 93, 94, 95, and possibly 96. The textbooks have to be changed again.

FERMI: Exactly what happens in the case of uranium and thorium is as yet not completely understood. These elements have unstable nuclei as shown by their natural radioactivity. When a neutron strikes, some catastrophe occurs that gives birth to a large number of artificially radioactive elements. Since the spring of 1934 we have been attempting to isolate chemically the carriers of these activities. We know that at least many of them are not varieties of uranium or of any of seven elements just below uranium in weight. It is still a matter of investigation as to whether this is proof that the new elements are heavier than uranium or whether some unusually complicated disintegration takes place.

DAVIS: I know that you and other physicists were discussing in Washington a few days ago some new experiments of Professor Otto Hahn in Berlin that indicate extraordinary release of atomic energy. That sounds exciting.

FERMI: These experiments have been confirmed in at least four laboratories in Europe and America. About two weeks ago Dr. Frisch in Copenhagen first observed these atomic fragments. And before we knew of his results, due to the time taken by the mail to reach this country, the same experiments were performed also at Columbia University and at the Carnegie Institution in Washington, and probably in some other places. At Columbia University we found that the capture of a neutron of only 1/30th volt energy can release from a uranium atom's nucleus 200,000,000 volts of energy, more than six billion times the energy shot into it. The difficulty in applying this practically is that the processes for producing neutrons have a very low yield.

Davis: The release of atomic power is a very important achievement. Perhaps we had better quiet the fears that anyone may have as to any danger of the world blowing up. As I understand it, the danger is very, very remote.

Fermi: That is very true, Mr. Davis. There is no cause for alarm. The work that I have told you about is but one of the many investigations that have been carried out in the last few years all over the world in order to get a better understanding of the intimate structure of matter. Whether the knowledge acquired will have a practical outcome, or whether it will remain limited to the field of pure science cannot at present be foretold. But this is not the question that physicists ask themselves. In a world that is sadly divided by material interests, it is comforting to see that beyond all barriers of nationality scientists find a common aim in the disinterested search for truth.

Fanfare in the Press

Professor Fermi's broadcast was probably unintelligible to most of his listeners. It was quiet, scholarly, reserved, factual. No ordinary citizen could have grasped the meaning of the momentous events of January, 1939. But their meaning did not escape those few trained members of the profession of journalism who specialize in the news of science. There is hardly a score of them in the United States and half of them are in New York. Two of the ablest and most active, John J. O'Neill of the *New York Herald Tribune,* and William L. Laurence of the *New York Times,* saw the meaning at once. They covered the story completely in their own papers, then later both wrote full accounts for national magazines. Complete with details and personalities, William Laurence wrote in the *Saturday Evening Post:*

"On Sunday, May fifth, on the eve of one of the greatest upheavals in man's history, the world learned about the discovery of a new source of power, millions of times greater than anything known on earth. A newly extracted natural substance, present in relative abundance in many parts of the world, but very difficult to isolate, had been found capable of liberating energy at such an unbelievable rate that one pound of it was the equivalent of 5,000,000 pounds of coal or 3,000,000 pounds of gasoline. In explosive power one pound of the new substance would be equal to 15,000 tons of TNT. Only one chief obstacle remained—to find a method for isolating the substance in large quantities, and scientists were hopeful that such a method would not be long in developing.

"The name of the new substance, a veritable Prometheus bringing to man a new form of Olympic fire, is uranium 235, or U-235 for short. It is a rare form of uranium, each 140 pounds of uranium containing one pound of U-235. It differs from uranium in its atomic weight, ordinary uranium being 238 times as heavy as hydrogen (the lightest of the ninety-two elements), whereas U-235 weighs 235 times as much as hydrogen. Hence the name. Even the existence of U-235 was not known until 1935, when it was discovered by means of a highly ingenious 'atomic microscope' by Professor Arthur J. Dempster, at the physics laboratory of the University of Chicago. There was not the slightest reason at the time to expect anything unusual from this newly found relative of the royal uranium family of elements.

"The complete story behind the story of this astonishing development, that may turn out later to be 'the greatest story in the world,' has until now remained largely untold. The story had its beginning about a year and a half ago, in Berlin, with experiments on uranium conducted by Dr. Lise Meitner and Professor Otto Hahn, a scientific team that had worked together for twenty years. Like many an explorer before them, among whom Columbus is the best known example, they were seeking a new route between two known points, and came instead upon a miraculous new continent of matter, as rich and wonderful in its way as the Americas proved to be many years after their discovery. And, like Columbus, these modern discoverers of a new continent of vast resources did not themselves realize the nature and extent of their discovery. This was to be determined by later explorers, largely in America.

"Meitner and Hahn had set out to repeat a famous experiment carried out by Professor Enrico Fermi, Nobel Prize winning physicist, who left Fascist Italy to continue his work at Columbia University. Professor Fermi had discovered a strange game of 'atomic golf,' in which atomic balls, known as neutrons (fundamental, electrically neutral building blocks of the universe), could be made to score 'holes in one' with much greater frequency if they were made to travel with slow speed, the 'hole' in this case being the nucleus, or core, of the atom.

Through-the-Looking-Glass

"The purpose of this game is to liberate part of the enormous energy locked up in the nucleus of the atom. In playing this game, using uranium as the 'atomic golf course,' Professor Fermi observed strange Alice-Through-the-Looking-Glass phenomena that did not seem possible. It appeared that in the course of this game new elements had been created heavier than the heaviest found in nature, elements beyond uranium, heavyweight of the natural components of the physical universe.

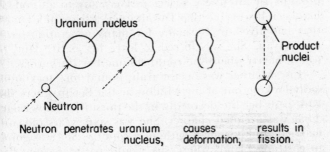

Neutron penetrates uranium   causes   results in
                    nucleus, deformation, fission.

"Meitner and Hahn devised a highly delicate 'atomic microscope' that enabled them to 'see' what was happening chemically on the 'atomic golf course' more clearly than could be done before, then proceeded to fire slow-speed neutrons à la Fermi at the uranium nucleus. And the result surprised and startled them so much that they believed some serious error had been made. They repeated the experiment, only to observe once again what they had seen in the first place—an 'atomic ghost' that had no business being there. Instead of an element resembling uranium they observed an element totally different, having an atomic weight only little more than half the weight of uranium. The 'atomic ghost' was seen to materialize itself, and lo, here, out of nowhere, appeared the element used in the taking of X-ray pictures of internal organs—barium.

A Deep Mystery of the Laboratory

"Barium! How the deuce did it get there? Where could it have come from? There definitely was not a trace of barium present when the experiment was started, and yet here it was. It was like placing a duck's egg in an incubator and suddenly seeing it hatch out into a chicken.

"Before a solution could be found to this scientific mystery of the first magnitude, Hitler's racial decrees

brought Dr. Meitner's career in Germany to an end. I
had been discovered that Dr. Meitner, a scion of a famil
that had lived in Germany for many generations, wa
not 'Aryan.' She was forced to leave her native land t
seek a haven where she could resume her life's work.

"Lise Meitner was on the train bound for Stockholm
sadly looking out of the window at the Berlin where sh
had spent her life devotedly in the pursuit of knowledge
That was a closed chapter. She was sixty years old, un
married, and a woman without a country. She was going
to a strange land, where she would try to resume her
work, her unfinished strange experiment, barium.

"She could not get barium out of her mind. Could i
have been an impurity? Dr. Hahn was the most careful
of chemists. He had been meticulously careful to exclude
any possibility of the uranium being contaminated with
barium, and yet, in spite of the most careful precautions,
the barium appeared, like Hamlet's ghost on the ram-
parts. Where could the barium have come from? Nothing
ever comes from nothing, and there had been no barium
there to start with.

"Lise Meitner's thoughts wandered far afield and kept
coming back to barium. Suddenly, what seemed at first
an idle thought, to be dismissed as daydreaming, flashed
into her mind. Barium has about half the atomic weight
of uranium. Could it be possible that the bombardment
of the uranium with the slow-speed neutron bullets split
the uranium atoms in two nearly equal halves, one of
which was the mysterious ghost of barium that appeared
in the experiments?

"She attributed the thought as most likely being due
to the strain she had been under during the past few
days. It was too fantastic to be true. For nothing like it
had ever happened before in the hundreds of thousands,
if not millions, of atom-smashing experiments in leading
scientific institutions all over the world, during the past

twenty years. Not even the most powerful atom-smashing machines in America, largest of their kind anywhere in the world, had ever succeeded in chipping off more than a small bit of an atom. Even an elementary student of physics knew that there was not enough power available anywhere on earth to split an atom in halves, particularly the heaviest of all the elements.

"She began jotting down figures on paper. Every well-informed layman knows by this time that the material universe is made up of ninety-two fundamental elements, beginning with hydrogen, the lightest, at No. 1, and ending with uranium at ninety-two. What makes the elements differ from one another is the number of positively charged electrical particles, known as protons, in their nucleus, or core. Thus hydrogen has only one positive electrical particle in its nucleus. Helium has two. Carbon has six, nitrogen seven, oxygen eight, and so forth. If helium were to be split in halves, each half would be not helium but hydrogen. If oxygen were to lose one positive particle (proton) it would no longer be oxygen but nitrogen. Mercury contains eighty positive particles in its nucleus and gold has seventy-nine; hence if one of these could be knocked out of the mercury nucleus it would be transmuted into gold. Similarly, uranium contains ninety-two, barium fifty-six, and krypton thirty-six positive particles respectively, in their central core. Hence, if uranium could be split by some process into two uneven pieces, of fifty-six and thirty-six units each, the broken parts would be, respectively, barium and krypton.

56 and 36 and Energy Undreamed Of

"Having scribbled the figures 56 and 36 on her note-book, Lise Meitner began doing a little more involved calculation. It takes tremendous energy to hold the unit particles in the central core of the atoms together. This is known as the 'binding energy' of the atom. If an atom were to be broken in halves a certain portion of this binding energy would be released, and, in the case of a heavy atom, the amount of such binding energy that would be released should be of tremendous proportions. How much? she wondered. With expert mathematics she quickly arrived at the result and then went over her figures to make sure. . . . Yes, she was right. If a uranium atom of ninety-two positive particles were to be split into two parts, one of which consisted of 56 (barium) and the other of 36 (krypton) particles the amount of atomic binding energy released would be the hitherto-undreamed-of figure of the order of 200,000,000 electron volts per atom, an energy 5,000,000 times greater than that released in the burning of coal.

"The figures before her overwhelmed her. She was experiencing sensations that must have been akin to those of Columbus when he first sighted land, without knowing exactly what the land was. Was it the East Indies? A mirage? A new continent of untold wealth? If her figures were right, and they could well be checked, she and Dr. Hahn had accidentally stumbled upon one of the greatest discoveries of the age. They had come upon the trail of what might lead to the shores of the Promised Land of Atomic Energy.

"When Lise Meitner arrived in Stockholm she did two things that started off a set of events as dramatic as any in the history of man's endless quest for new means of mastery over his material environment. First, she prepared a report of the results of her strange experiment for a scientific journal, so that scientists in other parts of the world, both inside and outside Germany, might take up the quest for an answer to the puzzle. Second, she telegraphed the gist of her findings to a scientist friend in Copenhagen, Dr. R. Frisch.

"It so happens that Dr. Frisch is the son-in-law of

Professor Niels Bohr, of Copenhagen, Denmark, one of the world's most famous pioneers in the investigation of the atom. Professor Bohr was at that time—it was January, 1939—in America, carrying on investigations with his colleague, Einstein, at the Institute for Advanced Study, Princeton, New Jersey, and also with his other Nobel Prize winning colleague, Fermi, at Columbia. Dr. Frisch did two things. He at once cabled the news from Dr. Meitner to Dr. Bohr in America, and he set to work repeating the Hahn-Meitner experiment in Dr. Bohr's physics laboratories at the University of Copenhagen.

"The news reached Dr. Bohr on or about Tuesday, January 24, 1939. He lost no time in communicating the startling developments to Dr. Fermi. These two master minds in modern science began making some calculations of their own. Without knowing the full details of Dr. Meitner's figures, they soon arrived independently at the same conclusions. Sure enough, if the uranium atom could be split into two pieces, the parts would fly apart like gigantic atomic cannon balls, the greatest ever produced in any laboratory, each fragment traveling with an energy close to 100,000,000 electron volts, or a total of 200,000,000 electron volts of energy, by far the greatest ever liberated anywhere.

A Surprise for the Physicists

"If their calculations were right then the 'atomic thermometer' of Columbia's giant atom-smasher should register the fact. They called together a conference of the Columbia atom-smashers, headed by Professor J. R. Dunning, under the general supervision of Dean George B. Pegram. For a day and a night they labored, preparing, testing, checking, observing. Then, on Wednesday, January twenty-fifth, their labors were finished—a tired group of scientists were anxiously standing around the 'atomic thermometer.' One of them pressed a button. Yes, the uranium atom was definitely being split. Little David was cracking nature's Goliath in two and forcing him to give up an enormous amount of his strength.

"It so happened that on Friday following the experiments there was to be held at George Washington University, Washington, D.C., a conference on theoretical physics in which Dr. Bohr, Dr. Fermi, and a select group of leading American physicists were scheduled for informal discussions on the latest developments in their probings inside the atom.

"There was nothing to indicate that anything out of the ordinary was about to take place when Dr. Bohr rose to speak that afternoon of January 27, 1939, in one of the lecture rooms at George Washington University. It took some minutes before the import of what he was saying, in low, even tones, had impressed itself on their critical minds. Had anyone other than the great Bohr, or another of his stature, uttered the words they were hearing it is doubtful if they would have taken them seriously.

The Atom-Smashers Get Busy

"Suddenly there was a commotion and the room became nearly empty. Calm young scientists, leaders in their field, never observed to show undue excitement about anything, were seen rushing to the nearest telephones. One or two science reporters present sensed there was something momentous in the air, but the young physicists were too busy to talk to them. Excitedly they got their colleagues in their laboratories on the telephone. Bohr has just reported something tremendous. Sounds fantastic, unbelievable, but they must get hold at once of a sample of uranium and repeat the experiment Dr. Bohr had just told them about. Columbia had already done it, but they must not lose time to do it on their own.

"In almost no time the giant atom-smashers at the Carnegie Institution of Washington, Johns Hopkins

DR. KENNETH J. BAINBRIDGE

DR. JOHN R. DUNNING, leader of the research team developing U-235, in the Pupin Laboratories at Columbia University

University, and a number of other leading scientific institutions, were engaged in a blitzkrieg against the uranium atom, hurling against it billions upon billions of atomic projectiles in the form of slowed-up neutrons. There was no sleep that night in January for any of these scientists in the laboratories of various parts of America, and they kept working on through the morning and into the afternoon.

"Finally, late Saturday afternoon, the news came through to the group of physicists at the Washington conference. It was true. The barium came as a result of the uranium atom having been split in two unequal pieces, releasing in the process a quantity of atomic binding energy 5,000,000 times the energy of burning coal.

"Then came word from Dr. Frisch by cable to Dr. Bohr that he had achieved the same results a few days ahead of the Americans.

"No sooner was the great barium mystery solved than another, equally baffling, presented itself. When the uranium is split in two parts a number of high-speed atomic bullets, in the form of neutrons, should be released in the process from the atom's core. If these neutrons were to be slowed down (slow neutrons are the most accurate) they should start a cyclic action in the manner of a string of firecrackers, one split atom automatically setting off another, which, in turn, would set off a third, and so on, in rapid succession, resulting in a terrific explosion.

"When no such explosion was observed, and no chain reaction in the manner of 'cosmic firecrackers,' the scientists set to wondering. There must be something that extinguishes the cosmic fire. What could that something be?

"Dr. Bohr, in collaboration with Dr. J. A. Wheeler, of Princeton, was the first with a theoretical explanation for the problem. Ordinary uranium, it had been found by Dr. Dempster in 1935, consisted of a mixture of three

DR. ERNEST O. LAWRENCE

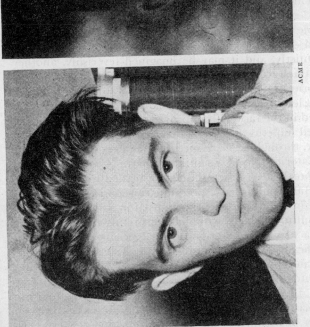

PROFESSOR ALFRED O. NIER

types of the substance differing in their atomic weight, the largest part consisting of atomic weight 238, while the two other types had atomic weights of 235 and 234, respectively. It had also been determined that the ratio of the uranium 238 to uranium 235 was 1 to 139—that is, in every 140 pounds of ordinary uranium there is one pound of pure uranium 235 (U-235), scattered so finely that the job of separation had up till then been regarded as impossible. Uranium 234 is the rarest of the three, existing in a ratio of 1 to 17,000 of ordinary uranium.

"It was the U-235, Dr. Bohr and Dr. Wheeler concluded on the basis of theoretical reasoning, that was starting the atomic fires going. The U-238 was the element that was quenching the fires. If only a sample of the U-235 could be obtained in pure form! But no such sample was available, and until that could be done the world could not know for certain.

"Quietly, and it may be imagined feverishly, another scientific race was set going in our leading scientific laboratories. The industrial research laboratories of the General Electric Company, fully realizing what was at stake, joined in the race with improved apparatus. And the race gained impetus by reports that kept trickling out of Germany, through a grapevine in which exiles from German laboratories played a significant part.

"Shortly after Lise Meitner was exiled from Germany, Dr. Hahn published a preliminary report on the experiment in a German scientific journal in which he confined himself to the facts, without interpreting them. Since the spectacular corroboration of the experiment, and its full significance, has been published in America not a word has come out officially from German laboratories. But in spite of the strict censorship, and the thick veil of secrecy, reports began trickling through, all fitting together the scattered parts of a jigsaw puzzle. By direct order of Hitler, according to the reports, some 200 of Germany's

greatest scientists were concentrating all their joint energies on the solution of the one problem—U-235.

"The problem of separating twins of the same element
so close to each other in weight was a formidable one and
required a considerable amount of experimental ingenuity for its solution. Credit for being the first in the
field with a tiny sample of the precious substance goes to
Dr. Alfred O. Nier, twenty-seven-year-old physicist of the
University of Minnesota. Shortly thereafter another,
slightly larger, sample was isolated at the General Electric research laboratories at Schenectady, New York, by
Dr. K. H. Kingdon and Dr. H. C. Pollock. Both samples
were rushed to Columbia University and submitted to
tests, and both provided experimental proof that Dr.
Bohr and Dr. Wheeler were right in their theoretical
predictions that it was the U-235 that had been split in
two and released the greatest amounts of atomic energy
ever to be observed.

"These first microscopic bits of U-235 may, therefore,
well be regarded in the not-too-distant future as the very
cornerstone of a new civilization. Fifty years from now,
when the present war may be but a memory, the generation then living may look upon this discovery as one of
the turning points in human history. Certain it is that
it will be regarded as one of the great discoveries in modern science.

"But nature has a way of tantalizing man by placing
before him a luscious morsel and then interposing seemingly insuperable obstacles between him and the desired
object. No sooner was the discovery made of the tremendous power-potentialities of U-235 than it was realized
that nature had locked it up so tightly with ordinary
uranium that it was, to all intents and purposes, impossible to separate it in pure form in large quantities. The
methods used for separating the first tiny samples at the

University of Minnesota and the General Electric Company yielded the substance at the rate of 1036 millionths of a gram every ten days, working twenty-four hours a day. At this rate it would take 26,445 years to produce one gram, and 11,995,074 years to extract one pound. It was, therefore, at once realized that the principal problem to be solved before atomic power could become a reality was to devise a method, or methods, that would make possible the extraction of U-235 in practical quantities.

"The prize at the end of the rainbow was in itself great enough to start a friendly scientific race among America's leading university and industrial laboratories. But this friendly race, usual among scientists as among the rest of mankind, assumed an ominous aspect as the tentacles of the swastika cast a shadow on the tranquil walls of our laboratories. For here again it was realized that, with all their superior equipment and ingenuity, the American scientists, because of the very limited funds available for research, were at a considerable disadvantage in working against scientists of totalitarian Germany, who had practically unlimited resources at their disposal. What if the Germans succeeded in attaining their goal? A few hundred pounds of U-235, even in a concentration of only 10 to 50 per cent purity, according to calculations, would place in German hands potentially the most powerful fuel ever dreamed of.

"It is the prevailing opinion among American scientists that, in spite of the enormously greater resources at the disposal of the German laboratories, they could not possibly solve the problem in less than ten years, and probably much longer. Yet developments in science move so fast these days that no one is willing to make definite predictions as to what might, or might not, be done in the near future.

The Problem of Isolating U-235

"Even now there are signs on the horizon promising considerably improved methods for the separation of U-235 in larger quantities. A number of new methods are being quietly developed in American laboratories, and one of them in particular, known as the "thermal-diffusion method," taking advantage of differences in temperature to separate lighter particles from their heavier components, is being thoroughly investigated as the most promising for the present.

"The development of this method furnishes another fine example of the fact that progress in modern science is the result of contributions by many scientists in many lands. The method was originally developed in Germany for other purposes a few years ago. Later it was improved upon in America. More recently, Professor W. H. Furry, of Harvard, Professor Lars Onsager, of Yale, and others, worked out by mathematics a theory for employing the method with greater efficiency. Taking advantage of all these contributions, Professor Wilhelm Krasny-Ergen, of the University of Stockholm, Sweden, designed an apparatus last summer which, he believed, would increase the yield of U-235 more than 12,500 times over present methods, provided certain chemical compounds of uranium could be produced.

"Unfortunately, the invasion of Norway brought Dr. Krasny-Ergen's work to a stop before he had even completed his apparatus, so that for the present it still remains a purely theoretical calculation, and with no one willing to swear that the theory behind the calculations is watertight. All that scientists are willing to say now is that 'it appears probable that it will work,' but that 'there may be several years of concentrated work needed before success is reached.' Even then, when U-235 is obtained, they add, 'there is the very serious problem of shielding the operators from the U-235's radiation.' The screens may have to be so bulky as to prohibit the use of the material as a lightweight power source.

"Moreover, practical scientists point out, even if the Krasny-Ergen method did work, a method that increases the rate of yield by 12,500 times would still be very slow, requiring some 350,000 days (960 years) for the isolation of one pound.

Future Power Possibilities

"However, still speaking theoretically, this would be true only for one unit of the apparatus. If the apparatus should be found to work, and scientists believe that it probably would, the problem would become largely an economic one. If it would take 350,000 days for one unit to produce one pound, then 1000 units would produce a pound in 350 days, and 100,000 such units, easy and cheap to make, would yield one pound of U-235 every three and a half days.

"In a country like Germany, with its totalitarian economy, the cost of any undertaking is a very minor consideration when the government decrees that it is vital for the national economy, and if the reports are correct, the Nazi government has so decreed.

"One pound of pure U-235 would have the explosive power of 15,000 tons of TNT, or 300 carloads of fifty tons each. But such a substance would not likely be wasted on explosives. A five-pound lump of only 10 to 50 per cent purity would be sufficient to drive ocean liners and submarines back and forth across the seven seas without refueling for months. And the technique that would be required for its utilization would be even more simple than the burning of coal or oil, according to present theories based on small-scale experiments.

"Just as coal needs a fire to release its energy, the U-235 would need only water. All that would be needed to start it would be to place it in water. The water would first be turned into steam and the steam would run powerful turbines.

"When all the water had been used up the process would automatically stop, until more water was supplied to start it again. A constant supply of cold water, well regulated, would keep the process going on for months, or even years, depending on the quantity of the U-235 present.

"The basis for these theoretical considerations rests on the discovery by Professor Fermi that neutrons when slowed down, by being made to go through water, become thousands of times more accurate in hitting bull's-eyes square into the hearts of atoms. Fast neutrons have tremendous speed, but no control. They pass right through, or by, atoms without hurting them. Neutrons slowed down to low speeds, the lower the better, gain in control what they lose in speed. They go straight for the heart of the atom, and once they enter it they have not enough energy to get out. In the case of the U-235 atom, because of its bulk and inherent instability, the slow neutron, on entering, splits it in half. The splitting, it is believed, automatically releases other neutrons, which, slowed down in turn, will split more U-235 atoms, starting a firecreacker action in a process that would be both automatic and self-regulating.

"The neutrons have a weight very close to that of hydrogen. Since two thirds of the atoms of water consist of hydrogen, the neutrons, on being made to pass through water, strike the equal weights of the hydrogen atoms, and in doing so yield up most of their energy, so that they are slowed down to speeds corresponding to energies of one fortieth of an electron volt (an electron volt is a very small fraction of an erg, or unit of work).

"On being slowed down the neutron is said to become 'tuned' to the central core of the atom, so that it heads straight for it. To use a golf analogy, the slow neutron behaves as though a golf ball were magnetized and aimed at a hole containing a powerful magnet. Even the poorest of golfers could, under such circumstances, make holes in one.

"To start the fires of atomic energy burning in U-235 it would not be necessary, according to theory, to provide neutrons from an outside source. What are known as 'free' neutrons are present everywhere in the universe. Cosmic rays that keep entering the atmosphere from the outside at all times during day and night, and minute amounts of radium present in the air, continually collide with the oxygen and nitrogen atoms in the atmosphere with such force that fast neutrons are liberated. When a piece of U-235 will be placed in water, these fast neutrons would therefore be slowed down and start the automatic release of atomic energy, as long as there was water at the proper cool room temperature. Hot water, or steam, would not slow the neutrons down sufficiently to be effective.

Energy Still Untamed

"Tremendous as the release of atomic energy from U-235 is, it must be realized that it constitutes only a very small fraction, less than one tenth of 1 per cent, of the total power contained in the U-235 atom if its mass could be completely utilized as energy. Each unit of atomic weight has an equivalent in energy of a billion electron volts, so that U-235, having 235 such units, contains the enormous energy of 235,000,000,000 electron volts, or 1175 times greater than the 200,000,000 electron-volt energy yielded by the splitting of the U-235 atom. In other words, if all the mass of one pound of U-235 could be converted into energy it would yield the equivalent in power of 5,875,000,000 pounds of coal. Stated in other terms, one pound of U-235 contains a total energy of 10,000,000,000 kilowatt hours of electricity, of which only less than one tenth of 1 per. cent, or 10,000,000 kilowatt hours, could be utilized by the splitting of the U-235 atoms with slow neutrons.

"Not even in the stars and sun is the entire mass of atoms converted into energy. It has been calculated that one thirtieth of a gram of water (there are 453.59 grams per pound), converted into pure energy, would yield enough heat to turn 1,000 tons of water into steam. In one whole gram of water there is a sufficient store of energy to raise a load of a 1,000,000 tons to the top of a mountain six miles high. A breath of air would operate a powerful airplane continuously for a year; a handful of snow would heat a large apartment house for a year; the pasteboard in a small railroad ticket would run a heavy passenger train several times around the globe; a cup of water would supply the power of a great generating station of 100,000-kilowatt capacity for a year."

The First Speculations

Meanwhile, John J. O'Neill had covered the same ground more sedately in *Harper's Magazine*. After reviewing the facts, Mr. O'Neill applied his long experience with scientists and his logic to present some deductions which today seem strangely prophetic. They were the first inkling, aside from the frightened fantasies of the uniformed, as to what might lie ahead for humanity as a result of these German, Italian, Danish, Swedish, British, and American researches. Pearl Harbor was still a long way off and so was Hiroshima. Mr. O'Neill wrote:

"Reference was made to the use of pure uranium 235 in the atomic energy process. It may be that this substance will never be used in its pure metallic state because of the probability that it would be entirely too active. It is more likely that uranium 235 will be alloyed with uranium 238, as it is probable that a mixture containing as little as five per cent of the 235 isotope, or perhaps even two per cent, may prove to be a very useful and easily controlled atomic energy fuel.

"A slab of the pure metallic uranium 235 would have fantastic properties in the presence of a neutron gas. It would look like nickel and would be very heavy, about 22 times as heavy as water. Its activities would belie its innocent appearance. If a person should bring his hands near this block of metal to grasp it he would very quickly draw back, because the metal would become very hot, perhaps incandescent as he approached. The water in his body would act as a slowing-down agent for the neutrons present, and the slowed neutrons would start the atomic disintegration process.

"If a slab of the metal were dropped into a tub of water, on the suspicion that it was a bomb and this was the best way to keep it from exploding, the result would be surprising, for there would follow an explosion like a volcano letting go. The water would slow down the neutrons and the atoms would start to explode in a chain reaction, making the metal incandescent and changing the surrounding water to steam in an extremely small fraction of a second.

"It is obvious from the foregoing that if uranium 235 is ever isolated in massive metallic form it is going to be highly desirable to keep it extremely dry and away from the neutron-water combination.

"It is probably necessary to have a mass of uranium 235 six inches or more in diameter if the chain reaction is to be maintained in it. With smaller masses it may be necessary to have a starting process in constant operation because too large a percentage of the secondary neutrons may escape.

"There is every indication at the present time that it will be possible to control the atomic energy process so that power can be drawn off in such quantities as can be handled safely. But there is a possibility that if we use o pure a sample of uranium 235 the processes may ke place at such a rapid rate that all the energy in a ass of the material may be given off in an instant before ontrol processes can become operative. If this condition ere brought about intentionally we should then have ot an atomic power source but an atomic energy explo- ve.

"As an explosive uranium 235 exceeds present explo- ves in destructive power to the same extent that this tomic power source gives more energy than is obtained om the burning of coal, or about 5,000,000 times as reat, weight for weight. If we take into account only hat small fraction of the mass of uranium 235 whose nass is transformed into energy, more than 3,000,000 imes as much energy is given out than comes from the urning of an equal mass of carbon in oxygen.

"Annihilation of one gram of matter (there are 453.6 rams in a pound) would release 62,500,000,000,000 foot ounds of energy. This would be sufficient to raise the mpire State Building (weight 303,000 tons) 20 miles igh. Or about a square mile of midtown Manhattan ould be raised several hundred feet high with no pro- isions for cushioning the shock on the return trip. This mount of energy would be released from about two ounds of pure uranium 235 which rapidly exploded ll of its atoms in a chain reaction."

And Imagination

So much of O'Neill's pondering was logical, based on he facts and on the assumption that U-235 could some- ime be obtained in pure form. Then he made a further assumption, perhaps more remote, that the violence of he explosion could be controlled and released slowly as needed for industrial use. He goes on somewhat imag- inatively:

"Speculating on the possible application of a discovery

is not an idle pastime. It is one means of evaluating the significance of the new development. It is the means of tentatively testing the ground that lies ahead on the course of progress. Courage, imagination, and a sound grounding in facts are prime requisites for useful endeavors in this field.

"It is unthinkable that we should fail to use constructively this new discovery of a way to release atomic energy. We should therefore thoroughly acquaint ourselves with its favorable and unfavorable aspects and, if the former exceed the latter by a sufficiently wide margin, prepare to utilize it to the fullest extent, making full provisions for all the adjustments that will be required in our economic, social, and political structures, national and international.

"Our present civilization is dependent upon energy. The extent to which we use energy is one of the indices of the state of advancement of our civilization. We have been lax in the task of distributing justly the benefits accruing from the increased use of energy, and as a result our economic structure is under a variety of stresses and strains. The greater the extent to which we use energy the faster is the tempo of our civilization. This will undoubtedly be true of the era of atomic power which is now dawning. We should therefore make all necessary adjustments to put our economic structure on the soundest possible basis.

"Power, energy, enters into almost every activity of our lives. Our principal primary sources of power are coal, oil, and gas. If we state all of them in terms of coal, then each individual in the United States uses the equivalent of 7.2 tons of coal per year, or 36 tons for the average family of five persons. Translating this into terms of electrical energy, at the average power-house order of efficiency of 1.44 pounds of coal per kilowatt hour, each individual in the United States consumes, or has con-umed on his behalf, 10,000 kilowatt hours per year, or 3,400 horsepower hours. This gives each individual 36.7 horsepower hours per day or 1.5 horsepower hours working for him every hour of his life. Probably less than 20 per cent is used directly in the home and the remainder is used in operating trains, ships, airplanes, automobiles, farms, factories, and a variety of forms of services for his benefit. Our energy bill, in round numbers, is about $3,000,000,000 a year. The largest fraction of this becomes part of the cost of the goods we consume. If atomic power did nothing more than cut the cost of our energy bill in half it would be a very valuable development. But this is only one of the minor blessings which it probably has in store for us.

"A relatively small quantity of uranium 235 installed in a heating plant in the home might supply enough energy to keep that house warm in winter and cool in summer as long as the house stands. A more probable development would be heating and air conditioning by electricity bought at such a cheap rate that installation of a home power plant would be uneconomical.

"Our automobiles might have installed in them at the time they are built a fuel supply that would last as long as the car. One might be able to travel as many thousand miles as he wished without having to bother about fuel bills. Oil bills might become a minor item, very much smaller than at present because the present gasoline engines would be replaced by quieter and more easily maintained steam engines with an extremely small oil consumption.

"Fuel costs for railroads, ships, and airplanes might be greatly reduced, thus reducing travel costs. Stratosphere travel might become common for airplanes, and we might make long journeys in much shorter time than is now possible. Railroads would probably stick to steam power because, with the fuel and smoke nuisance eliminated, it should be cheaper and more convenient than electricity.

"Extensive sources of cheap heat might bring about great changes in our agricultural methods. In our homes we could use a great many electrical labor-saving devices. It should be remembered, however, that only 10 to 20 per cent of the present cost of electricity is due to fuel costs. The complete elimination of this item would reduce the cost of electricity in homes in New York City, for example, only from 5 to 4 cents per kilowatt hour.

"Power might become a negligible cost item in our manufacturing establishments. Larger and more efficient machines, and more of them, might be used. Goods might become cheaper, though it must be borne in mind that electrical power costs now comprise only a very small fraction of the cost of goods. Engineering projects on a gigantic scale might become possible.

"Central power houses should continue in operation. Many industries which do not now use electricity in certain operations because of the cost of the current should be enabled to do so. Among them would be the heavy chemical and iron and other smelting industries.

"What are the economic effects likely to be? The first effect will be psychological. Many industries face a tremendously important cycle of change. Some will be established on a sounder foundation and others will be eliminated. There are so many, and such great blessings for everyone in the coming atomic-power era that we should try to see that no one suffers unduly in the transition.

"If atomic power can be developed cheaply, the coal-mining industry is going to suffer most. Should atomic energy come into general use, a necessary consequence would be that coal mining as an industry would cease. Coke production for by-products and the steel industry would presumably continue however as a part of the chemical industry.

"The oil industry would be hit temporarily, but would thank its lucky stars that it has invested millions of dollars in scientific research. Oil as a fuel may pass out, but oil as a chemical raw material out of which an almost unbelievably vast array of materials can be made may be in greater demand than at present. Our home, furniture, clothes, and even some of our food may be pumped out of oil wells in the near future.

"The railroads may pass through a very trying period. Coal comprises one-third of their revenue freight. If atomic power comes into general use this revenue will be lost. Railroads use about 80,000,000 tons of coal a year, one-fifth of the total amount mined. Atomic power would largely eliminate this expenditure, but this saving would hardly be sufficient to make up for the loss in revenue.

"Extensive changes would have to be faced by the automobile industry. The motive power might be changed from internal-combustion to steam, assuming of course that a satisfactory small-size power plant could be designed. In this case the most important change in design would be elimination of the fuel tank. The fuel supply for the life of the car would be built into it at the factory. The roadside gasoline and oil stations would go.

"The public utilities may have an intricate problem to solve. A new fuel that gives vastly more energy than coal, pound for pound, is bound to come laden with problems as well as opportunities."

And a Warning

But Mr. O'Neill knows that splitting atoms one by one is a long way from any such practical consequences and that decades of research must intervene. He closes cautiously:

"It would be unfortunate if the impression were given that atomic energy is going to be made available to us merely by the waving of a magic wand or the equivalent, in some minds, the undulating traverse of a fountain pen across a checkbook. There are many practical problems to be solved.

"In the first place it should be understood that this first process utilizing uranium 235 does not release the entire amount of energy represented by the full mass of the material, but only that portion of the total which is described as the binding energy of the nucleus and which amounts to about one-quarter of one per cent of the total mass. Even this, however, gives vastly more energy than the burning of coal of equal weight. The practical problem at the moment is the scarcity of uranium 235 and the difficulty of extracting it.

"Uranium 235 is obtained from the ores of ordinary uranium, which contains three-quarters of one per cent of uranium 235. The principal source of uranium is pitchblende, a heavy rock that looks like tar, and which contains 65 to 92 per cent of the metal as a black oxide. Nearly all of the mines from which this ore is obtained were located and developed shortly after the discovery of radium, which is also obtained from uranium. The largest pitchblende deposit is probably that in northwestern Canada, discovered a few years ago. There are two mines in Germany, one in the Belgian Congo, one in Australia, and one in Colorado, the latter having the uranium in a secondary form as carnotite. There is such a small market for uranium compounds at the present time that the prices are abnormally high. Granite rocks contain a small amount of uranium, and if the demand for the material is sufficiently great, many concentrations of the ore material will undoubtedly be found.

"Separation of uranium 235 from uranium 238 is difficult at the present time. It has about the same status now as did heavy water when Professor Harold C. Urey, Nobel Prize winner, of Columbia University, discovered it a few years ago. It was then the rarest substance on earth but today it can be purchased in heavy concentrations and in large quantities from a number of commercial producers.

"The cost of separating uranium 235 from uranium 238 may prove to be an economic barrier to the use of this substance as a means of obtaining atomic power on a practical scale. The reward for bringing down the price, however, would be so great that we can reasonably assume that this will eventually be done.

"After due deliberation in balancing the blessings, the possibilities, and probabilities, against the handicaps and dangers, the net results appear to be an indication that the discovery of the uranium 235 process for the release of atomic energy promises the dawn of a new era for mankind."

Science and Sabotage

The Race to Develop the Bomb

THE REICH was a year behind in developing the atomic bomb, according to an interview with a German scientist reported by Kathleen McLaughlin for the *New York Times*.

"On the day the war ended in Europe, Germany's production of the atomic bomb still was at least one year from realization. Such, at least, was the estimate by United States Army Air Force officials received yesterday from Dr. Hans A. T. Bomke, a German physicist now living in Munich, who was interrogated on details of the German program because he was associated with experiments in that field in 1939.

"As assistant to Professor Otto Hahn, director of the Kaiser Wilhelm Institute at Dahlen, Dr. Bomke and other scientists were drafted by the Nazis for the development of a high priority program promptly upon the outbreak of war. He was withdrawn by the Hitler regime in

1942 and ordered to work under pressure, he told Air Force questioners, doing research on ultra-short electric waves with the object of bringing Luftwaffe navigation instruments up to the level of progress revealed in captured Allied planes. This was our superiority in radar equipment, Army men commented, that Dr. Bomke and his associates succeeded in large part in equaling after two years of intensive effort.

No practical application of atomic forces was possible, he related, until 1919, when Lord Rutherford, English physicist and Nobel Prize winner, succeeded in transmuting the chemical elements by artifical means. Professor Hahn at that time was Lord Rutherford's assistant and therefore was familiar with his investigation.

"In 1939 Dr. Otto Frisch, a former colleague of Dr. Hahn, wrote an article predicting the future application of Professor Hahn's principle and suggesting that experiments with uranium bombs be performed on a solitary island in the Pacific to reduce the risk of the enormous damage the explosion of such a bomb would cause. Then began a race among the scientists of the world. Important contributions were made during experiments with uranium, in Russia by a Professor Kapitza, and in Germany by Professor Hahn's associates, Professor Werner Heisenberg, inventor of modern quantum mechanics, and a Nobel Prize winner, and Professor W. Bothe of the University of Heidelberg.

"Then came the war and the strictest secrecy instantly was imposed on this work. Similarly, in the Unitel States, many scientific research institutes became specialists in atomic destruction experiments, and proved to be the first to manufacture successfully the atomic bomb."

The Allies attacked German research by underground and from the sky. The most dramatic story was reported from Rhukan, Norway, by Barbara Wace of the Associated Press.

ACME

MME IRENE JOLIOT-CURIE, her husband, FREDERICK
JOLIOT-CURIE, and their two children, PIERRE and JEANNINE

"Nearly three years ago in the stillness of an Arctic midnight, nine youths of the Norwegian underground stole out of the snowy mountains into this beautiful valley of the Moon river and blew up a factory. Their daring sabotage may have changed the course of the war.

"It snagged Germany's frantic efforts to produce an 'atom bomb.' Kjell Nielsen and Claus Helberg, two of the raiders, told the story of the exploit today.

"They disclosed that as long ago as the summer of 1942, the underground knew that the Nazis were using a Rhukan factory to produce 'heavy water'—and suspected the heavy water was being used in research on the atom. (Heavy water is deuterium, or heavy hydrogen, which means hydrogen atoms of twice ordinary weight.)

"They said their sabotage—supported by the British— was accomplished after four of their party had survived unaided for four months in the mountain fastness of this Arctic region, where for five months of the year the sun never shines, and where the wind is so terrific that it has blown trains from their rails.

"Nielsen was among the first to suspect the Nazis' plan. He is a chemical engineer who formerly worked in the sabotaged factory.

"Two German scientists who worked with him, he said, told him that if they were certain the Nazis were using the heavy water in atom experiments they would refuse to cooperate, because of the threat to mankind.

"'When we got suspicious,' said Claus, 'the home-front leaders sent nine of us Rhukan boys to Britain to tell them about what was going on and what we feared.

"'There we trained, in Scotland and England, and learned about explosives and parachute landings.

"'Then in October of 1942, three companions and I parachuted into the mountains.

"'It was bad weather—the worst winter in fifty years. Five others were supposed to come along with us, but they couldn't parachute because of the weather.

"'So we camped in the mountains in a little ski-hut. We lived there four months, on one month's provisions, plus reindeer we killed ourselves.

"'We even learned to eat the stomach of the animal. That's a trick I heard from Canadians to get vitamin C.

"'It was a long time to wait up there with the weather so bad. For days we couldn't leave the hut. It was hard to keep warm. But I gained twenty pounds in those four months, and lost them when I got back in civilization.'

"The five others trained for the sabotage finally parachuted into Norway and joined them in February and the raid was carried out.

"Before the sabotage, Nielsen said, the Nazis here were producing 4.5 kilograms a day of heavy water. It was being exported, but Nielsen did not know where.

"One ferry carrying some of the product across Lake Tinnsjo was sunk. 'They lost much heavy water which took them six months to produce,' Nielsen said.

"Nine months after the raid, the Germans had succeeded in replacing the machinery. But a force of eighty American heavy bombers swept in between the towering mountains and did the job again."

The "Secret War" in the United States

The Germans, encountering difficulties in their research, endeavored unsuccessfully to spy on American progress. This story is told in an Associated Press dispatch of August 9, 1945.

"The FBI said today that five German spies sent to the United States after 1939 to learn of atomic bomb developments were persuaded to double-cross the Nazis and work as counter espionage agents.

"Several of the spies were intercepted in Europe and South America en route to this country and made double agents before they launched any espionage activities for

the Nazis, an FBI spokesman said. He would not disclose
their names.

"As a result of American alertness, the FBI said, no
sabotage of any kind was committed in an atomic plant.

"The German agents carried specific instructions from
the German High Command to get information on the
atomic bomb experimental program, the spokesman said.
One of the spies, who worked for the FBI as a double
agent for two and a half years, transmitted fake information on our atomic bomb program to the Germans and
in return received inquiries from Berlin which proved of
value to the FBI."

And Then the Bomb

THE FRONTIER of science on the atomic front had penetrated into the nucleus by 1940. It was now certain that
mass and energy could be converted into each other and
it was also proved that the neutrons which cause the fission of uranium nuclei reproduce themselves in the process—in other words that more neutrons are produced
when the uranium atom is broken. It was obvious that in
that case those released neutrons might break down neighboring uranium atoms so that the process would be repeated, as in a chain. It was quite possible that this might
occur with explosive force.

From this knowledge to the bomb at Hiroshima was a
long, difficult, expensive path. Outside of the men actually engaged on the problem and the responsible government officials, no one knew what was being done and few
had any certainty that any work was in progress. All work
subsequent to 1940 was conducted in absolute secrecy.
The fact that the work was successful was published on
Monday, August 7, by President Truman. The details of
the five years of research and a summary of the scientific
achievements which do not involve national security were
published by the War Department on Sunday, August

12. It is one of the most thrilling stories—if not the most thrilling—in the entire history of science. What follows here is taken from the War Department report.

The Principle of the Bomb

As expected, the bomb releases enormous amounts of energy which comes from the actual conversion of some of the nuclear substance of heavy atoms like uranium into energy when the nuclei are broken under the impact of a slow-moving neutron. In order to make this process self-propagating and therefore explosive, it is necessary to utilize as many of the neutrons that are produced by the fission to produce fission in neighboring nuclei. This is not easy. Some escape, some are captured by uranium atoms without fission, and some are captured by impurities. Special devices are used to avoid these losses. In actual fact the first nucleus that explodes sets off the others.

As in the prewar work, the isotope of uranium which weighs 235 is the one most susceptible to fission. Only 0.7 percent of uranium metal consists of this isotope. The problem of concentrating U-235 is of colossal proportions. Rare as uranium is among metals (about four parts per million in the earth's crust as a whole) early estimates indicate that the nuclear energy in the known deposits is adequate to supply the total power needs of this country for two hundred years.

Power Versus Bomb

"The expected military advantages of uranium bombs were far more spectacular than those of a uranium power plant. It was conceivable that a few uranium bombs might be decisive in winning the war for the side first putting them into use. Such thoughts were very much in the minds of those working in this field, but the attainment of a slow-neutron chain reaction seemed a necessary preliminary step in the development of our knowledge and became the first objective of the group interested in the problem. This also seemed an important step in convincing military authorities and the more skeptical scientists that the whole notion was not a pipe dream. Partly for these reasons and partly because of the extreme secrecy imposed about this time, the idea of an atomic bomb does not appear much in the records between the summer of 1940 and the fall of 1941.

"If all the atoms in a kilogram of U-235 undergo fission, the energy released is equivalent to the energy released in the explosion of about 20,000 short tons of TNT. . . . Even if only one percent of the theoretically available energy is released the explosion will still be of a totally different order of magnitude from that produced by any previously known type of bomb. The value of such a bomb was thus a question for military experts to consider very carefully."

With these prospects a Uranium Committee was set up under the National Defense Research Committee in June, 1940, but expenditures and progress were relatively small until December, 1941.

During 1942 a self-sustaining "pile," operated by nuclear energy, was first put into operation. Initially it operated at a power level of one-half watt, but on December 12 the power level was raised to 200 watts. It was the first time that a continuous chain reaction, operating entirely on nuclear energy, had been used.

Plutonium—A New Element

Another achievement of 1942 was the production of a new element: Plutonium, named for the outermost planet beyond the planet Uranus. It is produced from uranium by the absorption of a neutron. This gives it an atomic weight of 239 (uranium is 238) and an atomic number of 93. No such element seems to exist in nature and it has always been assumed that elements heavier than uranium would be unstable and incapable of long existence. This turns out to be true, for the plutonium is also susceptible to nuclear fission and the release of energy. In this it resembles U-235, but it is not an isotope of uranium, consequently has different chemical properties and therefore can be concentrated from uranium far more easily than U-235 can. "By the end of 1942 plutonium, entirely unknown eighteen months earlier, was considered an element whose chemical behavior was as well understood as that of several of the elements of the old periodic table.

"By January, 1943, the decision had been made to build a plutonium production plant with a large capacity. This meant a pile developing thousands of kilowatts and a chemical separation plant to extract the products." The plant was placed on the Columbia River at Hanford, Washington, designed, constructed, and operated by the DuPont Company. A pilot plant for the production of plutonium was built at Clinton, Tennessee. The Hanford, Washington plant, begun in 1943, went into operation in September, 1944, and the entire plant was in operation by the summer of 1945 . . . performing better than had been anticipated.

The Bomb Itself

The actual assembly of the atomic bombs was done at Los Alamos, New Mexico, on a mesa about twenty miles from Santa Fé. The sole means of approach was a winding mountain road. Yet in a matter of months, under the direction of J. R. Oppenheimer, professor of physics at the University of California, the laboratory was assembled and in operation. Three carloads of apparatus came from the Princeton project, a cyclotron from Harvard, two Van de Graaff generators from Wisconsin. Says the report: "Other apparatus was acquired in quantity; subsidiary laboratories were built. Today this is probably the best equipped physics laboratory in the world. . . . The end of 1944 found an extraordinary galaxy of scientific stars gathered on this New Mexican mesa.

"It is impossible to prevent a chain reaction from occurring when the size exceeds the critical size. For there are always enough neutrons (from cosmic rays, from spontaneous fission reactions, or from alpha-particle-induced reactions in impurities) to initiate the chain. Thus, until detonation is desired, the bomb must consist of a number of separate pieces, each one of which is below the critical size (either by reason of small size or of unfavorable shape). To produce detonation the parts of the bomb must be brought together rapidly. . . .

"The obvious method of very rapidly assembling an atomic bomb was to shoot one part as a projectile in a gun against a second part as a target. The projectile mass, projectile speed, and gun caliber required were not far from the range of standard ordnance practice."

The report does not give final answers but leaves the problem of bomb assembly as of April, 1943. That all problems were solved is obvious from the results.

The Men of Los Alamos

Under the direction of Dr. Oppenheimer were heads of seven divisions: theoretical physics under H. Bethe, experimental nuclear physics under R. R. Wilson, chemistry and metallurgy under J. W. Kennedy and C. S. Smith, ordnance under Captain W. A. Parsons (USN), explosives under G. B. Kistiakowsky, bomb physics under R. F. Bacher, and advanced physics under Enrico Fermi. Assistant to Dr. Oppenheimer in co-ordinating research was S. K. Allison. J. Chadwick of England and N. Bohr of Denmark spent a great deal of time at Los Alamos and gave invaluable advice. The report states: "For security reasons, most of the work of the laboratory can be described only in part."

DR. W. ALBERT NOYES, JR., DR. GEORGE B. KISTIAKOWSKY, and DR. ROBERT C. ELDERFIELD

The Meaning of the Challenge

Oh how comely it is and how reviving
To the Spirits of just men long oppressed!
When God into the hands of their deliverer
Puts invincible might
To quell the mighty of the Earth, the oppressor,
The brute and boist'rous force of violent men
Hardy and industrious to support
Tyrannic power, but raging to pursue
The righteous and all such as honour Truth;
He all their Ammunition
And feats of War defeats
With plain Heroic magnitude of mind
And celestial vigour armed,
Their Armories and Magazines contemns,
Renders them useless, while
With winged expedition
Swift as the lightning glance he executes
His errand on the wicked, who surprised
Lose their defence distracted and amazed.

from *Samson Agonistes* by John Milton

The New Force for Destruction

WITHIN HOURS of the news that a force as great as fire had been unleashed by man, air waves and printed page forecast predictions of destruction. Substance, strategy, and society were seen to be in peril of complete annihilation or at least revolutionary change.

Substance

As John W. Campbell wrote in PM on Tuesday, August 7, it was as if "a piece of the sun were placed on earth" and it might bring life or death to humanity. John W. Campbell is a physicist and editor of *Astounding Science Fiction Magazine*. His development of the field of scientific theory, which now commands the respect of leading governments, enables him to predict the following possibilities for destruction of our material way of life.

Frankly, I am scared. I'm scared because I fear people won't fully realize that, from this day on, war is impractical.

This isn't a new bomb. It's something that never was before. It's the power to reach the stars and the power to kill the human race.

It depends on us to decide which power we use.

This fear isn't new to me. For fifteen years, I've been sitting around thinking of this development, wondering whether mankind would have the wisdom to temper the knowledge it was certain to gain.

The description which has appeared of the test firing of the atomic bomb in New Mexico does not adequately indicate what the phenomenon actually is.

If our physical theories are correct, we can say definitely that this releasing of atomic power is not a bomb in the old sense—a sudden release of gases which cause destruction by concussion. It is an entire rearrangement of the surrounding territory. It is what would happen if, for an instant, a piece of the sun or some other flaming star could be placed on earth. Its temperature of perhaps 50 million degrees at the point of impact would not merely blast the surrounding soil; it would change its atomic structure.

The blinding flash described at the New Mexico ex-

periment represents the weak, enfeebled end of the total
energy explosion which would take place. Most of the
energy released would be totally invisible. It would be in
the X-ray part of the spectrum, because of the enormous
heat generated.

If a piece of iron is heated hotter and hotter, it first becomes dull red, then yellow, then white hot. Iron melts at
this point. If it is heated still hotter, the liquid begins to
boil as it becomes blue-white hot. If it were heated still
more, it would gradually begin to radiate violet, then
ultra-violet and finally X-ray radiation. In an atomic
bomb, the temperature would be so high that practically
pure X-ray radiation would be given off.

What happens at the point of explosion is that the
enormously hot material of the bomb almost instantly—
call it one-billionth of a second—heats the immediately
adjacent material, rock, steel or whatever, to a temperature approaching its own. This material changes from
a solid to a raging incandescent mass of violently stripped
atomic nuclei which blasts out of the inferno. . . . The
new atomic bomb would create a huge lava pit of molten
material, surrounded by an area of total destruction, a
secondary area completely burnt out, and third area
ruined by concussion.

Other speculation on secondary effects of such an unprecedented release of X-rays will have to wait for further
experience. Certainly, those rays could affect humans.
Also, the atomic changes in the immediate area of the
point of impact could create harmful radioactivity in
steel or rock.

One thing we know is that reconnaissance sixteen hours
after the bombing in Japan showed the entire area to be
under a pall of dust and smoke. Much of this dust was
undoubtedly due to condensed rock which had boiled in
the fury of the atomic blast.

This dust is so fine that it will take months for it to

settle out of the earth's atmosphere. If many of these atomic bombs are used, we can predict magnificent sunsets as the superfine dust drifts all around the world, coloring the sun's rays.

Let's hope it isn't sunset for the human race. It could be sunrise—if we're wise.

Yet, these warnings were not mankind's first thought of the dread shadows of an atom-generated future. United Press quoted from an address made by Pope Pius XII on February 21, 1943, at the opening session of the Pontifical Academy of Science and broadcast at the time.

Since atoms are extremely small it was not thought seriously that they might also acquire practical importance. Today instead such a question has taken on unexpected form following the results of artificial radioactivity. It was, in fact, established that in the disintegration which the atom of uranium undergoes when bombarded by neutrons that two or three neutrons are freed, each launching itself—one being able to meet and smash another uranium atom.

From special calculation it has been ascertained that in such a way [neutron bombardment causing a breakdown in the uranium atom] in one cubic meter of oxide power of uranium, in less than one-hundredth of a second, there develops enough energy to elevate more than sixteen miles a weight of a billion tons; a sum of energy which could substitute for many years the action of all the great power plants of the world.

Above all, therefore, it should be of utmost importance that the energy originated by such a machine should not be let loose to explode—but a way found to control such power with suitable chemical means. Otherwise there could result not only in a single place but also for our entire planet a dangerous catastrophe.

The warning of Pope Pius went unheeded. The force of the atom had to be used before a means to harness it had been found. Exigencies of the war, the need to save American lives, brought a new burden to men's hearts, a burden described in an editorial in the *New York Times* on August 12th.

One Victory Not Yet Won

Even the inevitable end of a great war cannot wholly lift from men's hearts the burden that was laid upon them last Sunday by the dropping of an atomic bomb on the Japanese city of Hiroshima. By their own cruelty and treachery our enemies had invited the worst we could do to them. Even so, no one could fail to realize that by this invention and this act humanity had been brought face to face with the most awful crisis in its recorded history. Here the long pilgrimage of man on earth turns toward darkness or toward light. . . . The atomic bomb is capable of all that has been predicted for it. Even more, it is in its infancy. This is the steam engine of Isaac Watts, the telegraph of Morse, the flying machine of the Wrights. This deadly two-billion-dollar toy is experimental. If its area of absolute and undreamed-of demolition is today represented by a circle with a diameter of two miles it will soon be more if we care to make it so and its ultimate destructive powers are beyond all imagination.

A new and awful meaning comes into the famous words of Prospero in Shakespeare's "Tempest":

> *The cloud-capp'd towers, the gorgeous palaces,*
> *The solemn temples, the great globe itself,*
> *Yea, all which it inherit, shall dissolve*
> *And, like this insubstantial pageant faded,*
> *Leave not a wrack behind.*

Urban civilization might be wholly wiped out, and such population as survives at all reduced to the animal level of many thousands of years ago. Perhaps the secret of the atomic bomb would thus be lost, and after some thousands of additional years a kind of civilization would be restored. A week ago this kind of speculation would have seemed to most people like something out of a scientific romance. It is not so today. The most level-headed and prosaic of us must face a reality that transcends the dreams of Jules Verne and the early imaginings of H. G. Wells.

Strategy

On the military front the implications of atomic warfare are as revolutionary as its powers of destruction of the materiel of war. In an article in the *New York Times* on August 10th, Brigadier General David Sarnoff, President of the Radio Corporation of America, said:

A powerful nation today feels relatively secure as compared with one of the smaller nations. But that security may be sheer illusion in the future. No nation will be invulnerable to attack. No Goliath will be safe. Indeed, a small aggressor nation might have ample resources to destroy a great nation. Scientists of a small country may conceivably be the first to discover answers to unsolved scientific problems of the present. The possession of such a secret weapon by a small nation would make it more powerful and more dangerous than its largest opponent who did not have it for instant use.

The predictions of this article, which was written sometime before the first use of atomic bombs, were repeated by Cesar Saerchinger, commentator for NBC and the American Historical Association in a recent broadcast.

Nothing seems so limitless as the capacity of humans to face terror; nothing so certain as their willingness to die —for causes as nebulous as most religions and as inconsequential as the Emperor of Japan.

But if the atomic bomb will not stop war, it has already changed all our previous concepts of military power. As Dorothy Thompson says, if Switzerland had the bomb and the Soviet Union didn't, Switzerland would be more powerful than Russia. But it is inconceivable that Russia will not have it—before very long. Indeed all nations with sufficient money to pay the scientists and sufficient resources to carry out their plans will have it. Worst of all, we won't know who has it. Thus the bomb will add immeasurably to the insecurity of life.

It will also alter the popular concept of war and, we may hope, finally destroy the last vestige of our belief in its virtues. Heroism, in war, will cease to exist; for war now is no longer against those who make war, but against the helpless, inarticulate, powerless mass of civilians. War with atomic bombs is a slaughter of the innocent, and hard to justify in patriotic terms.

The atomic bomb will make obsolete most of the weapons we now have, and which we have spent billions to develop. It should make an end of marching, rolling, and even flying armies, and turn most of our battleships into potential scrap. It will make silly all such concepts as an "international police force" to maintain world peace; also such puerile arrangements as the "de-industrialization" of Germany and Japan as guarantees of peace. Most of the peace terms imposed by the Big Three will be unmasked as barefaced robbery, imperialistic expansion, and exploitation of the newly weak by the newly strong.

We are assured that the atomic bomb is merely in its infancy. Indeed, mankind, by entering the atomic energy age, has achieved the power to destroy himself. Pious pledges that we, as the "trustees' of the secret, will use it to achieve the peace are futile so long as we are not willing to sacrifice our sovereignty and share it in common pool with the rest of the world. The only hope of the world is the world state. It is a slim hope.

Specific military problems and questions were raised by military observers for the *New York Times* and the *New York Herald Tribune* who saw twofold military problems of defense and strategy for not only this war but any world war which might devastate the nations.

The New Face of War

The new face of war was still veiled yesterday in the death pall above Hiroshima, but its features were chaos.

The atomic-energy bomb that fell on the Japanese homeland blasted immediately not only the enemy, but also many of our previously conceived military values.

The coupling of atomic-energy explosive with rocket propulsion marks what may be the ultimate triumph of the offensive over the defensive. There is today no apparent—certainly no immediate—answer to stratosphere rockets with "cosmic" warheads, save an answer in kind. This suggests the end of urban civilization as we know it. If they are to be preserved, cities of the future may have to burrow downward instead of upward; dispersion, rather than concentration, and tunneling into the earth rather than reaching upward into the skies may be forced in future wars.

And if it be one of the objects of armies and navies and air forces to keep war from one's own soil and to carry it to the enemy's, all of these armed forces as we now know them, become obsolete. Mass conscript armies, great navies, piloted planes, have, perhaps, become a part of history, the slow, long, tortured history of man's ascent from the mud.

Will the atomic bomb reduce the frequency of wars; or will we merely substitute push buttons for cannons? Will man disperse and go, mole-like, underground; will he seek out new methods of defense, new weapons of offense; will wars still end in the age-old way with men on foot facing men on foot?

Will armies and navies in the old sense be forever obsolete? Will wars be essentially struggles between the mass wills of civilian populations? Or will the armed forces of the ground, of the sea and of the air, armed with new weapons, employing new techniques, still bear the bloody brunt of battle?

These are questions that no man today can answer; and it is idle and harmful speculation to attempt definitive answers to them now, before the dust has even settled over Hiroshima.

It is true that in the long history of war the pendulum has swung periodically from offense to defense, from defense to offense; for every weapon there has been an answer and for every answer there has been another weapon. It is true that war has constantly become more and more destructive, more and more terrible —especially since the start of the industrial era. But it is also true that, although war has ended civilizations, it has never ended civilization; men have been slaughtered, but man, a persistent creature, goes on.

But it is precisely because with rocket propulsion we have extended the range and speed of projectiles to Wellsian figures and with atomic energy we have expanded the destructive effect of explosives to unknowable dimensions that it is futile to speculate today. At Hiroshima we unleashed nature itself, and our past experiences and accretion of knowledge cannot serve to comprehend the result.

Hanson W. Baldwin, *New York Times*

Atomic Bomb Said to Overthrow Basic Tenets of Military Science

Mankind stands at the crossroads of destiny.

The decisions which now confront the mind of man are the most important in his history. Upon those decisions hangs his continued existence on this planet.

If man can rise superior to the things he has created, if he can harness them to his service and keep the control of them from the hands of those of evil purpose among his kind, we may well be standing on the threshold of a true golden age of peaceful development, one in which the free forces of the intellect and of the spirit may rise to heights never before attained. If he cannot, this planet will vanish into darkness and roll on, a blackened cinder, through the limitless night of interstellar space.

This is no repetition of the warnings which have been written before the publication of the first use of atomic force as a weapon. Those warnings were based on the known nature of pre-atomic war. They were warnings of chaos and of terror, but they were not warnings of the end of the world, only of the end of a particular phase of civilization. They were warnings of a new Dark Age, out of which man might again have arisen after a few centuries of suffering. But the forces which man has now brought into play are forces which can be utterly destructive, so that no living thing may survive their loosing—if ever they are loosed in their ultimate power.

All that we knew of war before the coming of the atomic bomb is now in question. Attack with the atomic bomb is not blockade; it is assault, it is more than assault, it is annihilation. In this, it changes the face of war completely, and perhaps for all time. It sets aside the old theories of attack and defense. It gives to the surprise attack the power to destroy utterly, without warning. In the hands of a gangster state, it would be the weapon of international blackmail par excellence, for there is no defense against it at present, and there may be none for a long time.

Indeed it is hard to see how a civilization which can produce atomic weapons can defend itself against them, for the very size and extent of the industrial facilities required to produce them seems to deny the possibility of burrowing underground to hide—and even so, we do not know how deep one has to bury oneself to be out of reach.

Major George Fielding Eliot,
New York Herald-Tribune

Thinking in Washington, as reflected by James Reston in the *New York Times,* centered on our new and terrible responsibility to all mankind and our new role in the society of nations.

Dawn of the Atom Era Perplexes Washington

The atomic bomb has done more than produce the surrender offer of Japan. More even than that surrender itself it has startled Washington into a realization of the magnitude of the problems of victory at home and abroad.

For in that terrible flash 10,000 miles away, men here have seen not only the fate of Japan but have glimpsed the future of America. Before they had wholly synchronized our political and economic institutions with the age of steam, and while they were arguing over the urgencies of the age of air, they were suddenly confronted with the shadow-shapes of the age of the atom.

What are they wondering about? Well, they are wondering about a great many things they have taken for granted for a very long time. On the basis of today's news and tomorrow's possibilities, they are wondering about old ideas and old prejudices and even about what they had assumed were old truths.

They are wondering about the myth of the "immunity of the oceans." They are wondering what happens to the old theories about States' rights and labor's rights and management's rights and the farmer's rights in the atomic age.

They are thinking vaguely of the immediate responsibilities of the victor, of the occupation of Germany and Japan, of Americans controlling dozens and probably scores of islands in the Pacific Ocean, of Americans sitting on commissions that decide what ships pass through the Dardanelles and who controls the Danube, and what can and cannot move through the Kiel Canal, and who votes in Poland.

It is a time of questioning in Washington. Some men are disturbed by the forms of the unknown and others are inspired by the challenge. How are men to be employed in an era of atomic power when we could not even employ them in the age of electricity? Can we adjust our minds and our institutions to an increase of power that is so great that even now, without atomic power, we can produce as many goods as we did in 1920 with 12,000,000 fewer workers?

How are men who are full of prejudice and fear and selfish national desires to live together in a world that has atomic bombs but that has no generally accepted rule of law?

Several immediate problems are obvious. A decision must be taken about the size of the occupation forces in Europe, Japan, and the Japanese islands, and about the size of the standing Army and Navy we wish to keep. Only when this is done can the vast problem of demobilization be carried out in the most orderly and effective manner.

The size of our contribution of forces to the International Organization will have to be negotiated and approved by the Congress as one of the several steps necessary to implement our ratification of the San Francisco Charter.

Broad and imaginative steps will have to be taken to reconvert our industry from the tasks of war to the functions of peace and to transfer our economy in such a way as to encourage the highest possible level of employment.

Legislation will be necessary to tide over those men who are unemployed while the gigantic swingback to peacetime industry is being accomplished, and the most careful agreements will have to be made with other industrial States so that the general reconversion of the United Nations does not degenerate into a scramble for raw materials, shipping, and export markets.

Similarly, the race between essential supplies and anarchy in the defeated and devastated areas will have to be carefully planned if the United Nations are not to find themselves attempting to administer millions of starving and desperate men whose return to something resembling orderly conditions is in our primary interest. . . .

But beyond these pressing questions lie several which, in longer range, are equally as fundamental. Two of these will serve to illustrate the sort of problem that has been thrown up by the staggering events we have passed through in the last few days.

First, what happens to the United Nations' Security Organization in a world of atomic bombs? A week ago it was generally conceded here that the political realities of the world made it impossible to go farther than the San Francisco Charter goes toward creating an international organization that could force all nations, large as well as small, to abide by fixed rules of international law.

Today many men here are becoming convinced that in spite of these political realities, the scientific and military realities since the atomic bomb necessitated our creating, or at least working far harder than we have in the past toward the creation of, such a rule of law in the world.

The mere possession of this bomb by the United States, Britain, and Canada undoubtedly will strengthen the diplomacy of these three countries in any attempt they may make to help organize the world in accordance with their principles. But first they must decide together how they want to organize the world and whether the time has not come for them to reach a much closer military and political understanding than they have ever thought necessary or possible in the past.

In short, the end of the war is just the beginning. We have fought and won the freedom to work out our own future. But it must be worked out not in the old world, which is gone, but in a new world which will test our character equally as much as did the war itself.

Social

This test of the national character was further analyzed by Marquis W. Childs in his United Features column, "The State of the Nation," in the *New York Post* of August 10th.

That blinding flash of light on the New Mexico desert and in crowded Hiroshima fills us with terror and horror. The cynic at the club round table said:

"Well, it's just like giving loaded machine guns to a cage full of apes and then turning them loose in the streets."

But it fills us with awe, and with wonder. It is like the feeling we have when we see a star fall across the night sky. A crude hand, an ignorant, unknowing hand has grasped the stuff of which the universe is made. These scientists, for all that they produced this thing, are almost as ignorant of the root cause as are we ordinary mortals.

You can read between the lines of the account of that testing on the lonely desert and see that they were not at all sure what was going to happen. Their conflicting reports on the effects of radiation after the bomb has exploded confirm their doubts.

It calls to mind the remark of a wise and philosophic Britisher who has seen this entire war from the inside in Washington and London. At the center of power, he nevertheless seems to have been less corrupted by power than most individuals who are so exposed. He had just come from lunching—this was a year and a half ago—with three scientists who were working on the atomic project. He reported that conversation as follows:

"They tell me that perhaps they will not be able to stop the explosion when once they produce it; that quite possibly it will go on to tear apart at least the planet on which we live. I'm afraid I could not regret it too much. If that should happen, as I understand it, death would be painless and instant and those still unborn surely could not complain. Perhaps the human experiment has been a mistake."

He was not being either cynical or funny. He spoke out of the infinite sadness which came from his knowledge of the suffering and horror which man has inflicted on man in this terrible conflict.

It is the supreme tragedy of this moment—that the new discovery, which dwarfs every physical achievement of the race until now, had to be used first for the destruction of human life. It was used to create more fear and hate. Women and children as well as men, undoubtedly by thousands, are still crying in agony and terror because the mind of man has unloosed the force of forces.

This is why those responsible for unleashing the new power must meet in solemn awe at once to control its use as the responsibility not of a nation or a group of nations, but of the race itself. The obvious suggestion has been made that the entire project be turned over to the new United Nations Organization.

It seems to me that this is too big a burden to pile on an organization not yet in being. We cannot wait until the new league is ready to take on such a load. Every moment that goes by increases the danger that this will become a matter of competition among all the nations.

The primary responsibility belongs to those who have evoked the new force. A working partnership of Britain, Canada, Australia, and the United States did the job. Let responsible representatives from these countries meet at once to serve as trustees until the new league is prepared to take over.

Like curious children, we have forced the lock on the forbidden door. Now, unless we mean to destroy ourselves, we must guard the entrance.

Forcing the lock, loosening the powers of atom energy, we have sowed seeds of hate and Americans may yet "reap the whirlwind," as Hanson W. Baldwin concluded in an article "The Atomic Weapon" in the *New York Times* on August 7th.

Yet when this is said, we have sowed the whirlwind. Much of our bombing throughout this war—like the enemy's—has been directed against cities, and hence against civilians. Because our bombing has been more effective and hence more devastating, Americans have become a synonym for destruction. And now we have been the first to introduce a new weapon of unknowable effects which may bring us victory quickly but which will sow the seeds of hate more widely than ever. We may yet reap the whirlwind.

Certainly with such God-like power under man's imperfect control we face a frightful responsibility. Atomic energy may well lead to a bright new world in which man shares a common brotherhood, or we shall become—beneath the bombs and rockets—a world of troglodytes.

With all other nations we shared the responsibility to make possible a rebirth of civilization. As Dr. Zorbaugh stated in a feature presentation "The Atomic Bomb—The End or Rebirth of Civilization?" over WNEW (New York) on August 10th:

The problem we face is this: During the years we must wait for science to harness atomic energy in the interests of civilization, can we prevent atomic energy from destroying civilization? The atomic-rocket threat of annihilation might well precipitate an armament race such as this world has never seen. How long could our economy stand up to such a strain? How long before our standard of living was depressed to the point at which men found themselves slave-laborers to the atom? Faced with a future that might at any moment disintegrate in a series of atomic explosions, how long would men cling to the long-range values and goals around which, surely if haltingly, we have built our civilization? Living with so drastically uncertain a future must profoundly change man's psychological and social outlook—cause man to live for the present rather than the future, for himself rather than the community. No government could afford to let control of atomic energy out of its hands. Holding it, the power of government would inevitably be heightened and centralized. How long could democracy stand up to such centralized power? With nations viewing each other over rocket-trajectories, like frontiersmen with their hands on the grips of their six-shooters, knowing that at the first sign of trouble, survival depends upon beating their opponents to the draw, how long would what is left of international morality stand up? I am no alarmist; these are real possibilities for the civilization of our generation un-

less we immediately seek and find ways to control the
destructive potentialities of atomic energy. Obviously
every nation and every individual within every nation
must bend will and energy to the formation of an international comity of nations that will remove the threat
of war. However, there is little in human history to encourage the belief that this can be acomplished by a
form of international government alone. It must be accomplished by attacking simultaneously the sources of
frustration and hostility in our community living which
periodically are projected in war. In this attack we will
have to lean heavily upon social science. Governments
must give the same support to the training of social scientists and social science and research that they have to
training and research in the physical sciences. Statesmen
must look to the social scientists for guidance as they
have to the physical scientists. Physical and social science
must work together

There were physicists who predicted that the splitting
of the atom would cause the disintegration of the physical
universe. The atom has been split and the physical universe maintains its stability. It is the social universe the
stability of which is threatened. The prevention of the
disintegration of our social universe is the fateful challenge the age of atomic energy throws down to our generation.

Into A New World

SPLITTING the atom is like discovering the other half of
the world—the biggest half.

Harry M. Davis, writing in the *New York Times
Magazine,* said:

The power of the atom has been unleashed. For better
or for worse we have entered upon a new era in the history of mankind. The dreams and speculations that have

been with us since the Curies discovered the amazing radioactive powers of the atom have become stern reality in the proving grounds of New Mexico and the streets of Japan.

The development is of Promethean significance. Generations millenniums hence may look back upon these years when atomic energy was first put to work in the same spirit in which we now think of the less well documented occasion when man first learned the use of fire.

Fire is a terrible destroyer, and so, today, is atomic energy. But fire is also the basis of the industrial civilization we now know—fire controlled in the boilers of our power plants, in the furnaces of our steel mills and smelters, in our automobile engines and in our jet-propelled and propeller-driven aircraft. The energy within the atom may well be the basis of an entirely new kind of civilization. . . .

Tremendous labors—probably greater than those involved in creating the atomic bomb—lie before mankind in harnessing this and new awe-inspiring power. It is impossible to foresee and predict how, and in fact whether, this will be done. Consider the millenniums from the first use of fire to the gasoline engine. Yet certain speculations seem plausible.

Speculation began as soon as the first successful atom-splitting experiments had been reported. Before censorship choked off the voicing of dreams, a number of people had given us a preview of the world as it might be. Among the most articulate was Dr. R. M. Langer, Research Associate in Physics of the California Institute of Technology, quoted in *PM*.

The Strangest Is Yet to Be

U-235 can change the face of the earth in peace as well as war. The power behind the atomic bomb can be harnessed to produce the Utopia that men have dreamed of through centuries of war, depressions, famine, and disease.

A scientist predicted five years ago that development of U-235 could bring within a century a world in which there is no need for war; a world in which there are no houses, railroads, or highways.

Dr. R. M. Langer, physics research associate at the California Institute of Technology, said five years ago in *Collier's* magazine that U-235 could create a civilization in which man would dwell underground for better living; where national boundaries would be obsolete because of swift travel; and in which meaning of the gold standard would be lost because of decreased living costs.

"U-235 is marvelously compact and incredibly easy to manage," Langer wrote. "It can be used to incubate eggs or to give off a white hot incandescence. It can be turned on and off like an electric light. It can be exploded with a violence beyond anything known on earth, and it can be stored, without deterioration, indefinitely."

Langer said U-235 is a special type of uranium, one of the three heaviest elements. U-235, a fuel of remarkable intensity, is so powerful that a pound of it is equal to the power of $5,000 worth of coal, he said. Compared with costs of electricity at one cent per kilowatt hour, it is worth $100,000 per pound. Production will be cheap, he said.

Because energy will be so cheap, freight and passenger transportation will become public utilities, he said.

The most amazing change the atomic wonder will bring will be man's independence of the sun for health and food production.

"Any country, with any climate, at any time of the year, on very small acreage indoors can grow what it needs to feed and clothe and provide shelter for its citizens," Langer said. "The citizens need only contribute according to their talents; administrative, manipulative, or technical services for a small fraction of their time."

Langer said people will choose to live underground in homes heated and completely surrounded by U-235 insulation and the added protection of the earth. They will sleep in perfectly insulated homes, and pick their breakfast fruit from indoor, dust-free, sterile plants. They will cook food in a few seconds in high-frequency cookers.

"Light is generated (in the future home) by fluorescence which occurs around U-235 and is piped under the house through transparent plastic sheets along the interiors of rooms," Langer said. "The household supply of U-235 is stored and used slowly in the chamber where plants are grown. Appropriate portions are automatically delivered through a tube-distribution system to stations where they are needed to provide heat or power for machinery or cooking.

"The new generation will take much of their recreation out of doors; for shelter and rest they may retire to their underground apartment. The problems of air conditioning will be reduced to a minimum by the insulation of the earth and perhaps by a surface swimming pool which would serve as a roof.

"Their plants will be grown under artificial heat and light, using the technique of hydroponics, in the water that flows through the rocks just below their underground ranch."

Langer said U-235 homes will have elevators to the earth's surface. Families will travel short distances in automobiles powered by small chunks of U-235 in a water tank inside the car, he said. Neutrons within the U-235 will split atoms and the U-235 will burn, turning water into steam for turbines which put the automobile into motion. There will be no roads, except for freight trucks, he said, for the automobiles will absorb all driving shocks.

The automobile of the future, he said, would be "suspended from an overhead axle so that it banks itself on turns and permits the occupants to write letters or do chores while under way." Langer envisioned these automobiles as "a spacious room or rooms of transparent plastics."

Railroads will be obsolete. All long-distance travel will be by propellerless airplanes which will rise vertically and be independent of atmosphere to keep them aloft. The planes, he said, "will depend on a remarkable property of U-235 not yet described. This property is a by-product of its energy generation and consists in the ejection of high-speed particles. Such a process can be used as a means of propulsion in the same manner that the ejection of a stream of water can be made to cause a lawn sprinkler to rotate.

"The ease of transportation and, still more, the refreshing independence of service and storage made possible by the compactness and convenience of U-235 will cause our cities to spread out all over the countryside, even to territories barren and now uninhabitable. Agricultural lands will be returned to nature and wild life will share in the bounties of U-235."

"Humanity might well become a single, uniformly spread community, sharing as neighbors the whole surface of the world," Langer wrote.

He warned, however, that "in the hands of criminals and eccentrics" U-235 would be a "weapon of extraordinary power." The "destructive potentialities of U-235," he said, "are great enough to make it imperative that the citizens of the future be better educated than they are now with respect to their social responsibilities . . . Society will have to keep track of all the uranium produced and refined and take action at once against any individual who tries to accumulate a dangerous supply."

Admitting that none of the ideas he envisioned have yet been worked out in practice, Langer declared that the difficulties were those of detail, and that, if anything, the picture he drew was "not imaginative enough."

"For the immediate future," Dr. Langer concluded, "practical applications of U-235 open a new world for invention and ingenuity. . . . There will be no end of applications to our wants and needs and they will contribute to the richness of life and bring rewards of wealth and satisfaction."

Now that men's imaginations have been turned loose again, we have predictions of—

Atomic Planes

Aircraft scientists today envisioned an atomic-age plane capable of flying many times around the world at speeds faster than sound without refueling.

The National Advisory Committee for Aeronautics said "many years of research and development lie ahead" before a sucessful atomic engine for planes emerges.

But when it does emerge, it will fill a need long recognized in experimentation with faster-than-sound (supersonic) flight "for more efficient sources of energy."

Secret NACA research for the Army and Navy had disclosed that engines "which operate through simple chemical reaction of fuels" are characterized by high fuel consumption "and a staggering waste of energy."

NACA scientists estimated that an atomic engine will generate 8,000,000 times as much energy as present jet propulsion engines. And because of the small amount of "fuel" needed for atomic engines, the plane of the future will be vastly superior to present aircraft in payload capacity and range.   *United Press*

Robert D. Potter explained in a CBS broadcast how atomic power will enable jet planes to soar into airless space.

The great gift of atomic energy for transportation is that it puts into a compact space energy that far excels the power of modern jet planes or even of the rockets that soon may be leaving this earth for other planets.

Both jet planes and rockets need oxygen in their fuel supply because they burn gasoline or equivalent fuel. Therefore, both jet planes and rockets must either pick up their oxygen in flight or carry it with them in the form of a gas or liquid. If a gas is used this means strong heavy cylinders that can store the oxygen under high pressure. If liquid oxygen is used it requires a refrigerating machine that will maintain the liquid at a temperature of 360 degrees below zero Fahrenheit.

Yet, if planes or rockets operate with atomic power they will need no oxygen at all for combustion, because the uranium fuel is not burned in a chemical sense. These planes or rockets on atomic power could go anywhere outside the earth's atmosphere. Moreover, the power released in their motors would be millions of times greater than anything now employed.

The take-off speed and power of Germany's V-2 rockets has been computed to be one-tenth the energy needed to escape from the gravitational pull of the earth. If such rockets could have a source of energy one million times greater than they have now, they would easily lift themselves, passengers, and freight into interplanetary space.

In that day truly will come transportation between the planets that has always been called visionary.

Today that vision is on the threshold of reality.

Tiny Engines for Future Autos

An automobile engine no bigger than a man's fist was forecast yesterday by William B. Stout, past president of the Society of Automotive Engineers and research director of the Graham-Paige Motor Corporation, in analyzing the potentialities of atomic power as revealed in the new military bomb. He emphasized that progress in utilizing this superforce for automotive transportation must be conducted through slow and careful processes.

"This startling innovation opens a whole new field of power supply and may revolutionize many of the present methods of obtaining power," he said. "Like all new discoveries of great significance, the factor which would prevent its use as a source of power for automobiles, at the present time, is lack of knowledge of control of the energy of the atom. Long study and experimentation lies ahead before practical application in transportation units can be expected.

"The scope and adaptability of atomic power eventually will have a very wide range. Not only will motor vehicles be propelled by this energy but ships, planes, railway trains and virtually any form of transportation now in use.

"Another important feature will be the size of the engines. I believe that these units, placed in passenger cars, will be no bigger than a man's fist after they have passed through the refining stages needed to assure their practicability."

Mr. Stout asserted that it was still too early to speculate on the popularization of atomic power, primarily because of the danger involved in its use before all elements of control are definitely understood. "I expect to see gasoline used as long as I live," he added.

"The revelation of the possibilities of atomic power means as much, and even more, to peacetime progress than it does to warfare," he continued. "There is no doubt that vast economic gains will be derived and gigantic power-producing machines will be turned into pygmy units, while giving superior performance.

"Up to the present time we automotive engineers have not given much thought to the utilization of atomic energy in our field, as we did not believe it would be a practical factor in transportation for many years. Recent events, however, have brought this element much more into the foreground. But I do not think it can be safely harnessed into motor vehicles for at least ten, and possibly twenty, years.

"However, the main point is that it is here to stay, with a future of vast benefits to mankind."

New York Times

The imaginative prophecies seem restrained in the light of predictions made by sober and responsible men when they consider the use of atomic energy in place of our familiar fuels.

What Price Imperialism?

The fabulous energy released by the invention of the atomic bomb seems destined "fairly soon" to replace power produced by coal, oil, and water, the Duc de Broglie, eminent French physicist, said today in commenting on news of the bomb, which dazed and fascinated Paris today.

The Duke added that naturally this was far more important than the war or the defeat of Germany. He thought that it could be compared only with the discovery of fire by primitive man.

He estimated that the energy obtainable from a disintegrated atom would be about 200,000,000 times as great as that in the most powerful explosive hitherto known.

The Paris newspapers seemed uncertain today whether the announcement of the new missile exceeded the Pétain trial in importance. Some thought not; others quickly began hunting experts to tell them whether President Truman's statement on the bomb could really be true. The answer given was yes and that Mr. Truman did not exaggerate for propaganda purposes.

At the Foreign Office, where they had long been racking

their brains over the future of the Ruhr, the Saar, and the Rhineland, officials concluded that they might as well go fishing, too. Why acquire gray hairs over the Ruhr and the Saar if "fairly soon" coal is to become useless and abundant heat and energy are to be derived from systematically disintegrated atoms?

A few weeks ago General Charles de Gaulle said that it was necessary that the Rhine, "from one end to the other," should be in French hands, and he claimed Cologne as part of the French zone of occupation on the ground that invasions had started there. It is now asked, however, whether it is worth while to make a fuss about the Rhine as a barrier against an enemy crawling along the ground when future wars, if any, will be fought with atomic bombs.

In official offices are men who have spent years studying the relations between oil fields and the power of nations, all lately hunting feverishly for new oil supplies. They asked themselves today whether the time had come to roll up their geological maps and to revise many a policy since the quest of oil seemed to become in the future purposeless.

If a few atoms could be pulverized between now and winter and the released energy distributed in heat, France would need no longer to worry about getting 6,000,000 tons of coal from abroad.

"The invention of the atomic bomb is a great event for the destiny of the world, an event that in augmenting immensely the power of man also terribly increases his responsibility for the use he makes of it," he said.

"Twenty-five years ago a kind of super-chemistry was born, a chemistry of artificial transmutations which prolong and generalize radioactivity. This new chemistry concentrated on not groups of atoms, as did its predecessor, but the grouping of infinitely small bodies that form the nuclei of atoms."

Invulnerable to chemical reactions, these bodies correspond to Lavoisier's conception of simple bodies 150 years ago, which still remains true except when intervention takes place by methods that twentieth-century science has taught.

"Today we can penetrate inside the atom. This operation exacts and can liberate amounts of energy 200,000,000 times as great as that of the most powerful explosives. Yet we could so proceed only with atoms isolated in experiments in the most delicate laboratories. Only recently we did not know how to set in action in this way a large quantity of matter though we foresaw that the peculiar properties of the atoms of the heaviest elements, like uranium, would soon make this possible. Now we know that this final obstacle is overcome.

"It is too early to measure all the consequences. But here is a source of energy for all uses. It will be the motive force of tomorrow. Plans for machines to use this force have already been patented. In industry it will bring a fabulous revolution.

"Doubtless we shall no longer have to seek far and wide the raw materials coveted by nations. For now the new alchemists will have tools for the transmutation of materials not only theoretically but practically."

Harold Callender, *New York Times*

Among wonders and portents too numerous to mention, the following discussed by John T. O'Neill in the *New York Herald Tribune,* stands out: first, because it is based on facts and figures; and also because it concerns daily living and the common man's purse.

Atoms to Make Energy Virtually Free

Release of atomic energy is the most gigantic and important achievement of the human race in conquering its environment. It can be received as a blessing that will

make it possible for the human race to create a close
approach to an earthly paradise in its home on earth—
if used with wisdom . . .

All the freedoms and comforts which man enjoys can
be reduced to terms of energy available to him with which
to work out his ideas. When he had to depend on the
energy of his muscles his work was endless and his freedoms few.

Coal, when we learned to use it as a fuel and source of
power, brought the present power age which made it
possible for man to have days of leisure in his week, hours
of recreation in his days, and at the same time provide an
era of plenty in the matter of necessities and a vast array
of luxuries and comforts.

The amount of power now used in the United States
gives each person the daily equivalent of 37 horsepower
hours of energy. On the basis of human work output this
is equivalent to each individual in the country having
seven slaves working for him every hour of the day.

Atomic energy will increase vastly the energy available
to us. Uranium gives off 3,000,000 times as much energy
as an equal weight of coal. It will not be 3,000,000 times
as cheap because of processing expenses. If we are able to
get the advantage of only one-tenth of one per cent of this
output, coal will be more than 1,000 times as expensive
as uranium.

With such a tremendous leeway atomic energy unques-
tionably will be made extremely cheap—like "free air" at
the service stations.

Industrial projects on an almost free energy basis, in
factories operated to a large extent by robots, will be able
to turn out a mass production of goods unparalleled by
anything we have done heretofore. In time a tremendous
unemployment problem will be created which will make
the depression seem like a busy period unless we make
arrangements to prevent it, and these arrangements can

be devised along engineering lines. We will tackle tremendous national projects. One may be a new vacuum tube transportation system in which we will travel to the coast in half an hour.

Atomic energy will be used first in power houses, our present establishments, where it will be transformed into electricity. Our homes, factories and offices will be heated by electricity. There will be no coal bin or furnace in any cellar. Houses will not have chimneys. They will be air-conditioned. They may be artificially lighted at all times.

Our automobiles eventually will have atomic energy units built into them at the factory so that we will never have to refuel them. They will be operated by steam engines of a new type. There will be some delay in providing these automobiles as a way must first be found to shut off from passengers the tremendously powerful radiation—much more powerful than the hardest X-rays. This can now be done but the weight or bulk of the materials required is too great to meet practical considerations. The problem is far from being insoluble.

Steamships and locomotives operated by atomic energy will be practical in a short time. So will very large airplanes. Airplanes powered with atomic energy will be able to stay in the air for any length of time as far as fuel is concerned—for a lifetime if the ship will hold together.

There are a host of operations that could be performed directly by atomic energy, such as cooking food, by a process even simpler than electricity, as not even wire connections would be required. But it is possible that in the home electricity will be used instead.

In a relatively short time we will cease to mine coal. The gasoline service station will disappear from the road sides. The coal industry will disappear, but the oil industry will remain, not as a fuel producer but as a producer of chemical products such as synthetic rubber, plastics, and a host of other substances.

With vast amounts of cheap energy available to handle excess water we may find it cheaper to mine the ocean for a great number of the mineral substances for which we now dig holes in the ground. It also may become the source of new types of food supplies.

The technical effects of the world going on a new energy basis will have international repercussions. On the economic side the war has been directed toward control of oil and mineral supplies of the world. Campaigns and territorial changes have been based on oil control. Now oil will fade out of the picture. There will no longer be strategic supplies of minerals as atomic energy will make it possible to work the poorest grades of ores that are very widely distributed.

Advance in Medicine

Some of the basic principles of atomic physics discovered during work on the atomic bomb probably can be applied to the cure of cancer, Dr. C. P. Rhoads, director of Memorial Hospital, said yesterday during a conference to announce the founding of a new cancer research institute.

"A change in the biological system by the use of rays is important in all biological work," he said. "X-ray and radium already are used to cure cancer. Our increased knowledge of atomic physics will be valuable in learning the causes and cures of the disease."

Development of the atomic bomb was mentioned by Alfred P. Sloan, chairman of General Motors, whose Sloan Foundation is endowing the new institute, as a graphic illustration of what concentrated research can accomplish.

Sloan said he became interested in cancer research after his designation as a trustee of Memorial Hospital a year ago. The Sloan-Kettering Institute for Cancer Research will be organized in conjunction with the Memorial

Cancer Center. The Institute, Memorial Hospital, and the Dr. James Ewing Hospital, to be built by New York City at a cost of $1,500,000, will make it the largest center in the world devoted exclusively to the study and treatment of cancer.

Cancer is only one disease which may be defeated by atomic research. Thus phosphorus, artificially made radioactive by the "atom-smashing" cyclotron, is being tested against leukemia.

According to Bruce Bliven, in *The Men Who Make the Future*:

Atomic research has given us an inexpensive radium substitute which can be used for many purposes for which radium or X-rays are used and for important new purposes for which radium cannot be used.

The cyclotron can make 300 artificially-radioactive substances, in other words synthetic radium, each with its own peculiar properties. Of these 300, some 30 have been used with notable success.

The cyclotron is the most wonderful medical tool since the microscope. With artificially-radioactive substances one body organ can be treated without regard to other organs. Thus radioactive phosphorus is used to treat a serious bone marrow disease called palycythemia, in which the blood's red corpuscles multiply abnormally. Radioactive phosphorus is also used in certain types of leukemia.

In experiments on laboratory animals high concentrations of radioactive substances have been created in tumor (cancers), with very low concentrations in nearby tissues.

PM

In medicine, Dr. Cornelius P. Rhoads, director of Memorial Hospital, said atomic research had already been invoked experimentally for the last five or six years. Atom smashers have been used to make elements radioactive, so that a radioactive iodine, for example, can be studied in the body to measure the functioning of a thyroid gland. In treatment, atomic research has been utilized only in leukemia, a form of cancer, in which radioactive phosphorus, prepared by use of an atom smasher, is fed into leukimic tissue. But damage occurring to healthy tissues as well has been a major hazard thus far. "We have had plenty of atomic energy as far as medical purposes are concerned in radium," Dr. Rhoads said. "The problem is not to get more of it, but to control it."

Medicine pioneered in seeking uses of atomic energy through radium emanations and cyclotron (or atom smasher) products, the Medical Information Bureau of the New York Academy of Medicine pointed out, although present uses are principally in physiological studies. "Almost anything that happens in science is grist for the mill of medicine," the bureau added.

New York Herald-Tribune

Meanwhile, business men and economists were urgently considering the possible changes wrought by U-235 in commerce and industry.

In business circles in this country there is also much speculation—particularly among the men who control coal and petroleum, hydro-electric power, and natural gas. Their whole world has suddenly been faced with the possibility of a new source of energy and they've been discussing it busily since its announcement. Many of them refused to make any statements directly but most of them agree that a production of the new energy commercially would depend upon one consideration and that is the relative cost. Many of them doubted that atomic energy could be developed at a profit for private enterprise and they cited the cost of radium production, which is $30,000 a gram or about $12,000,000 a pound under present conditions.

Most of them skirted the fact that the production of atomic energy is not a private enterprise and probably will not be for a long time.

                                    Don Goddard, *NBC*

Peter Kihss, in the *New York Herald-Tribune,* gave Charles E. Wilson's views:

Charles E. Wilson, president of the General Electric Company, said that thus far "we have evidence that atomic energy in tremendous quantities can be released and controlled, at least to the extent of causing the release to occur at a desired time."

"It is probable that as the development is carried along," Mr. Wilson said, "we will find ways and means of controlling and using this form of energy as a source of heat for direct use, and perhaps for special purposes such as, for example, supplying power to drive an airplane, an ocean ship, or a locomotive."

But, in addition to technical problems to be solved, Mr. Wilson emphasized that "only time will tell whether future developments will permit atomic energy to be made available at costs which will allow its general commercial use."

The nation's anthracite industry, with a $400,000,000 investment in mines which provide fuel to heat 6,000,000 homes for some 35,000,000 individuals, also took a conservative view of the future. The weekly bulletin of the Anthracite Institute, 101 Park Avenue, said:

"It has been stated that coal could produce over 3,000,-000 times as much energy if used atomically, instead of in combustion. Obviously, this would revolutionize the generation of heat and power, since at this ratio, one-sixth of an ounce of coal would equal the annual fuel require-

ments of an average home, and twenty tons would replace
current annual anthracite production.

"However, there are three unanswered questions which
lead to the prediction that it will be many years before
the breakers are torn down to make room for atomic factories.

"The first is, can atomic energy be controlled and directed? The second is that uranium and the other materials now reportedly being used all have the heaviest,
most complex atoms which are relatively unstable and
comparatively easy to split. Carbon, on the other hand,
has one of the lightest, least complex atoms, which would
indicate much greater stability. The third all-important
question is how much would it cost to process a piece of
coal, or, in fact, any other material into a form that made
it capable of heating a house?"

Cost of Atomic Energy

The peacetime role of atomic energy will depend upon
one consideration—relative cost. This is the conclusion of
industrialists and engineers who have been weighing the
consequences to business of the epoch-making breakdown
of the uranium atom.

Energy is now obtained for the most part from coal,
petroleum, hydroelectric power, and natural gas. Con-
sumers of energy are constantly weighing the relative cost
and pertinent advantages of one source of energy over another, and base their utilization of one or the other upon
such comparisons.

For what is known about atomic energy, the cost factor
will preclude its use for all except certainly highly specialized purposes, as in chemical and metallurgical processes, where unprecedented temperatures are required. It
took $2,000,000,000 to perfect and produce the atomic
bomb. Even if most of this money went into research and
plant construction, the conclusion is inescapable that the

price of this energy source will compare, or perhaps greatly exceed, that of radium. . . .

Even though a pound of the material providing atomic energy possesses the energy of 6,000,000 tons of coal, as has been suggested, its use would be prohibitive if it is to cost $12,000,000 or more, considering that new utilization equipment and techniques would be required.

Until the method of producing atomic energy has been revolutionized and brought down to a low figure, therefore, it is likely to provide a source of thermal energy in extremely concentrated form only for highly specialized industrial purposes.

Even if production costs of the new atomic energy material are ultimately brought down to a level which would make commercial use feasible, there will still be little likelihood that two great sources of energy, petroleum and oil would be relegated to industrial oblivion.

Gustave Egloff, vice president of Universal Oil Products and a leading authority on petroleum technology, pointed out yesterday that about 50 per cent of the petroleum industry's annual output is "safe and secure" from competition from atomic power, pointing out that nearly half of petroleum consumption is for purposes other than power.

"Atomic power—as an economically competitive substitute for gasoline for ships, planes, cars, and other vehicles—still appears to be on a long road ahead," he said.

"However, assuming that time comes, the oil industry still will be needed to provide lubricating oils for the machines driven by atomic power. Wax and other by-products from petroleum still will be on the market and other uses may be expected to be developed by research."

He said the petroleum industry was "watching very carefully" every source of energy with the ability to provide power and that it "welcomes discoveries convertible into practical use which will shorten the war and develop new uses in the peace period."

He described development of the atomic bomb in three years as "literally a scientific and technical miracle."

Among recent developments credited to research Dr. Egloff directed was a "cheap" means of producing triptane, a super plane fuel with several times the power of 100-octane gasoline.

While coal is used chiefly as a fuel, it too, is a raw material for chemical products. Some 200,000 commercial products and chemical compounds stem from bituminous coal.

According to Dr. M. Lelyn Branin, technical consultant for the Bituminous Coal Institute, the atomic energy development" probably will have little effect on the use of coal during the lifetime of present adults."

Dr. Branin said that "eventual utilization of atomic energy for peacetime purposes does appear to be most promising," but added:

"It will undoubtedly be generations before the atom will make all of the nation's steel, power the nation's locomotives, generate the electricity or furnish the billions of hours of industrial horse power that coal does now, let alone heat the nation's homes."

Dr. Branin estimates America's coal reserves at more than 3,000 years' supply and describes them as "the greatest single storehouse of raw chemicals in the world."

Journal of Commerce

Upheaval?

America's industrial backbone will not be "vaporized" by the harnessing of atomic energy for peaceful uses, in the opinion of the men in Washington who are close to the new power development.

Leading industrialists in the nation also foresee slight change in the productive means in the nation for many years to come. Instead of viewing the atomic power as a threat, likely to close coal mines or make present electric power plants obsolete, they envision the control of the atom as a means for new production developments in a realm of science and engineering that will become a top layer of industrial growth over the present method used in America.

Coal, gasoline nor electricity are never likely to power a rocket to the moon, the officials concede, but a dozen rockets to the moon powered by atomic energy will not alter the need nor the uses for the ordinary types of fuel and power which the world is dependent upon today. There are few, if any, instances in the industrial growth of the world, it has been pointed out, where one discovery or development completely replaced another. The development of the wireless and the growth of radio did nothing in the way of retarding the use or need of the telephone. There is no reason to feel, the nation's scientific leaders believe, that atomic energy will ever do away with the demand for present power sources.

Estimates on the length of time it will take for the atomic power to be controlled and directed into industrial and commercial uses vary from a generation to a few years. American industrialists, however, have constantly crossed up their scientific colleagues by the speedy development of new findings into productive economic undertakings. If the growth of atomic power is a lengthy one government control will probably be responsible.

This control was declared essential by President Truman in his announcement of the atomic bombing of Japan and it is looked upon by most of the nation's leaders as a wise policy at the present time. If more knowledge and greater control measures are forthcoming in the near future there is the possibility of industrial demand altering this policy. Control of the atomic energy as a war weapon, however, will undoubtedly always remain under

Government supervision, or under the supervision of the United Nations.

Announcement of the successful harnessing of the atom brought to the forefront the whole matter of Government control of scientific research and development. Senator Kilgore's visit yesterday to the White House was for this purpose. He is the sponsor of a bill to place in Government hands all research and, in addition, the control of patents. Industry opposes any such sweeping Federal interference. The atomic bomb project, however, is a Government development, with patents, plants, and scientific know-how firmly held by the Government. Scientific research and development under Government control is, therefore, an established fact today.

Fantasy, fear, and hysterical predictions have all been part of the future discussed in connection with the atomic bomb disclosure. Scientific leaders admit they are probing in the dark in certain respects in connection with the astounding development they have secretly nurtured for the past three years. To the layman, they appear detached in relation to the consequences of their discovery but this, they also admit, is partly due to war-time secrecy and the fact that their own minds are far from clear regarding the eventual scope of their discovery. They are not disturbed, however, by the fear of world disintegration or of cataclysmic disturbances. They are in full control of what they have developed so far and they are already taking the measured steps which some day will lead to less destructive use of a new and amazing form of energy.

New York Sun

As people—half blinded by the varicolored flash of the bomb itself—we groped for solid facts and firmly based opinions, seeking anchors for our minds.

The column "Topics of the Times" of the *New York Times* reflected this:

The mathematician is the lucky one. To give you an idea of the future atomic engine he scribbles a few figures and signs on the corner of his newspaper, and you have the whole story, complete, precise, unanswerable. But we, poor laymen, trying to define this new miracle in ordinary words and pictures, only end up by raising more questions than we can answer.

Automobile engines of the future may be the size of a man's fist. Yes, but will the human fist be strong enough to hold the steering wheel on that automobile?

A cup of atomic fuel may carry a ship the size of the Queen Mary across the Atlantic. Yes, but who will want to spend two hours crossing the Atlantic by ship when he can do it by rocket in three minutes?

An atomic fuel supply the size of a brick may carry a plane several times around the globe. Yes, but will there be a terrestrial globe to fly around?

Apologies are due Mr. Churchill's opponent in the former Prime Minister's own constituency in the recent election. Among those to express regrets should be Mr. Churchill himself. He has said about the atomic revelations that we must pray that these "awful agencies" may be made to conduce to world peace and prosperity.

Now it will be recalled that Mr. Churchill's opponent in the election was a virtual unknown whom the dispatches came very near to calling a crackpot. The principal plank in his platform was a universal working day of just one hour.

Half a century ago there were economists who believed a four-hour working day enough to supply everybody with the basic needs and comforts. A dozen years ago the more ardent spirits among the Technocrats argued for a working day of forty minutes. Their calculations were based on the development of Giant Power, by which they mean the skillful utilization of existing energy sources. They did not convince everybody.

But today with the infinite potencies of atomic energy there cannot be the least question that Mr. Churchill's opponent for the House of Commons was right. The amiable crackpot now sees the world's mobilized scientists cracking away at the atom and permits himself to crack a smile. It was what he had in mind all the time, no doubt.

But it is no smiling matter at all, this new energy source for lifting the burden of toil from the backs of mankind and raising men to a plane of well-being hitherto undreamed. It is not a smiling matter because such a tremendous change in the common man's condition cannot be effected without social transformations of the very first magnitude. The history of the world since the French Revolution has been the history of the Industrial Revolution, which is, at bottom, the story of steam. But the steam engine is a little boy's wooden locomotive against the harnessed atomic engine of the future, and the difference in resultant industrial and economic revolutions should be the same.

Proved Fact and Scientific Prediction

How Soon Will the Atom Be Harnessed?

PETER KIHSS, writing in the *New York Herald Tribune* three days after the first bomb had crashed upon Hiroshima, reported the results of a canvass of the nation's leaders.

A long road in research still lies ahead before atomic energy can be harnessed into constructive uses for mankind. . . .

Fuel, transportation, and medicine are the fields which offer the greatest promise, at this sighting, for the long-range benefit of a humanity given command of the titanic forces hitherto locking together the universe's fundamental elements. . . .

In scientific circles, expectations are that the earliest peace-time adaptations of atomic energy will be for large units, such as ships, aircraft, and power houses. These would, first, make possible use of large chunks of uranium at a time, and, second, would be more readily protected against the intense radiation generated, probably by using heavy shields of lead.

Ironically, it is the problem of obtaining relatively small amounts of energy, to propel such smaller units as automobiles, that is expected to require the longer period of time. And in these units, another difficulty will be development of practical means to protect drivers and passengers without loading excessive weights of water or paraffin. One suggestion is that screens of such material as cadmium might be developed. Cadmium is one of the elements said to have a peculiar power for absorbing neutrons which are part of the emanation that would be hazardous.

Princeton University physicists, chemists, and engineers held a get-together on the subject, and produced a statement that "the new era of atomic power can be subjected to a process of development that can be evolutionary rather than revolutionary." Professor Leigh Page, acting head of the department of physics at Yale, said, "we now have something in our hands which, if we do not use it wisely, will mean the end of the human race." Dr. Serge Korff, director of physics research at the New York University College of Engineering, said: "The public should not become unduly alarmed. This development has been placed in unusually competent hands, those of men who are unselfish and non-political."

Sir James Chadwick, chief British scientist in the bomb project, was interviewed by the Associated Press.

He said there was a possibility that within about ten years atomic energy could be used for industrial purposes.

The Nobel Prize winner in physics in 1935 also declared that the atomic bomb was not strictly a British-American secret, asserting that any nation could learn the secret in about five years of experimentation, assuming it had access to the necessary raw materials.

"I think this is a very serious point," he said.

Sir James was chief scientific adviser to the British members of the American-British-Canadian policy committee that developed the bomb that wrecked Hiroshima and Nagasaki in Japan.

The work of this committee, he told a press conference, was confined to developing atomic energy for purely military purposes and very little attention was paid to the industrial possibilities. However, he said it would be "nearer ten years than fifty" before the secret of harnessing this new power for industrial purposes could be found, although there were many new problems to be solved.

He declined to say whether the three plants now producing the atomic bomb in the United States could be used for development of industrial atomic energy.

Meanwhile the United States Chamber of Commerce in its regular weekly report told its members that this new discovery would not immediately revolutionize industry, and that the "early" replacement of present sources of energy—coal, oil, gas, and water power—was out of the question. The organization said it had gone into this aspect of the question with other physicists.

A new Army publication provided an authoritative statement on the Government's view of the status of research:

One may guess that technical developments will take

place along two lines. From the military point of view it is reasonably certain that there will be improvements both in the processes of producing fissionable material and in its use. It is conceivable that totally different methods may be discovered for converting matter into energy since it is to be remembered that the energy released in uranium fission corresponds to the utilization of only about $\frac{1}{10}$ of one per-cent of its mass. Should a scheme be devised for converting to energy even as much as a few per-cent of the matter of some common material, civilization would have the means to commit suicide at will.

The possible uses of nuclear energy are not all destructive, and the second direction in which technical development can be expected is along the paths of peace. In the fall of 1944 General Groves appointed a committee to look into these possibilities as well as those of military significance. This committee (Dr. R. C. Tolman, chairman; Rear Admiral E. W. Mills (USN) with Captain T. A. Solberg (USN) as deputy, Dr. W. K. Lewis, and Dr. H. D. Smyth) received a multitude of suggestions from men on the various projects, principally along the lines of the use of nuclear energy for power and the use of radioactive by-products for scientific, medical, and industrial purposes. While there was general agreement that a great industry might eventually arise, comparable, perhaps, with the electronics industry, there was disagreement as to how rapidly such an industry would grow; the consensus was that the growth would be slow over a period of many years. At least there is no immediate prospect of running cars with nuclear power or lighting houses with radioactive lamps although there is a good probability that nuclear power for special purposes could be developed within ten years and that plentiful supplies of radioactive materials can have a profound effect on scientific research and perhaps on the treatment of certain diseases in a similar period.

We find ourselves with an explosive which is far from completely perfected. Yet the future possibilities of such explosives are appalling, and their effects on future wars and international affairs are of fundamental importance. Here is a new tool for mankind, a tool of unimaginable destructive power. Its development raises many questions that must be answered in the near future.

What Can Atomic Power Do?

Here, said Science Service, is what atomic energy could do if and when it is ever made fully available to work for man.

Smashing the atoms in one pound of water would create enough energy to heat 100 million tons of water from freezing to boiling temperature.

A breath of air would operate a powerful airplane for a year continuously.

A handful of snow would heat a large apartment house for a year.

The pasteboard in a small railroad ticket would run a heavy passenger train several times around the globe.

A teacup of water would supply the power of a great generating station of 100,000 kilowatts capacity for a year.

If the atomic energy in matter is made fully available for mechanical use, all other forms of energy would be antiquated, such as fuels and explosives. Dams and electrical transmission lines would be as outmoded as stagecoaches.

These estimates were made before the war (1934) when physicists were just beginning to visualize the tremendous potentialities of atomic research. They were published in *The Advance of Science,* edited by Watson Davis and published by Doubleday, Doran and Company.

Certain other uses for this new control over the atom are anticipated in another Science Service note:

The possibility that the Nazis might make a surprise use of radioactive poisons in a "particularly vicious form of poison gas" was considered early in the American scientists' atom-splitting experiments. Defensive measures were planned.

Radioactive poisons resulting from atom splitting were first mentioned in May, 1940, in a report of a committee of the National Academy of Sciences. They develop as the chain reaction of uranium-splitting proceeds and have, in practice, turned out to be "the most troublesome feature of a reacting pile." They differ chemically from uranium, so it was believed it might be possible to extract them and use them "like a particularly vicious form of poison gas."

This idea was developed in a report written by Dr. E. Wigner and Dr. H. D. Smyth of Princeton University on December 10, 1941, the day before we declared war on Germany. These scientists concluded that the fission, or atom-split, products "produced in one day's run of a 100,000 kilowatt chain-reacting pile might be sufficient to make a large area uninhabitable."

Radioactive xenon, radioactive iodine, and some twenty-eight other chemical elements, all highly radioactive, are produced when uranium is split by fission. The safe disposal of these poisonous gases, so as to avoid endangering the territory surrounding the uranium-splitting plants, was a troublesome problem. The scientists were able to solve this as well as to plan for defense against possible use by the enemy of radioactive poisons produced by uranium fission.

Where Uranium Supplies Are Found

Dr. Albert Einstein believes "it will probably take many years" to channel the enormous powers of U-235, but he thinks that other substances might be found, "and probably will be found," to accelerate its commercial use.

Uranium, more than 1,000,000 times as common as radium, is, reports Science Service, classed by chemists as a minor metal but now perhaps playing a major part in atomic bombs, occurs in various chemical forms in widely scattered countries of the world on at least three continents, North America, Europe, and Africa. Pitchblende, a form of uranium oxide, is mined in the Belgian Congo, in Bohemia in Czechoslovakia, and at Great Bear Lake, Northwest Territory, Canada. Carnotite, a uranium and vanadium salt of potassium, is found in Utah and Colorado.

Nearly the entire world output of radium-uranium ore prior to the war was mined at Great Bear Lake and in the Belgian Congo. . . .

The German supply of radium-uranium ore, during the war, was the relatively small amount available from St. Joachimsthal in Czechoslovakia. The Germans did not use the Belgian refinery at Oolen, near Antwerp, because there was no ore for it. The stocks at Oolen, including all of the radium and part of the uranium, had been moved to the United States before the invasion.

During the European war, the United Nations were in a favorable position as regards radium and uranium. These countries possessed an estimated two-thirds of the world radium supply and three-fourths of the uranium. Also they controlled approximately 95 per-cent of all the known ore reserves.

The carnotite ore mined in western Colorado and eastern Utah yields radium, uranium, and vanadium. The production did not meet domestic needs, however, and considerable radium salts, radioactive substitutes, and uranium oxide and salts were imported.

Plans for Development and Research

An indication of the rapidity with which refinements of the atomic bomb itself have been made lies in a report

that the bomb dropped on Nagasaki made the Hiroshima bomb, dropped three days earlier, appear "obsolete." It is said that more plants for the construction of
atomic bombs are being built at Oak Ridge, Tennessee.
The University of Chicago has announced plans for two
new institutes for the study of nuclear physics and metals.
Establishment of the institutes will take to Chicago two
Nobel Prize winners, Dr. Enrico Fermi, self-exiled Italian
physicist, who will become professor of physics at the
University, and Dr. Harold C. Urey, as professor of chemistry.

The Politics of Atomic Power

WITHIN a few hours after the bomb fell on Hiroshima,
men and women all over the world were thinking of the
"social engineering"—the building and management of
organizations—which is necessary before we can make
atomic power humanity's servant.

We Must Discuss . . .

said the official Government publication on atomic
power.

Because of the restriction of military security there has
been no chance for the Congress or the people to debate
such questions. They have been seriously considered by
all concerned and vigorously debated among the scientists, and the conclusions reached have been passed along
to the highest authorities. These questions are not technical questions; they are political and social questions,
and the answers given to them may affect all mankind for
generations. In thinking about them the men on the project have been thinking as citizens of the United States
vitally interested in the welfare of the human race. It has
been their duty and that of the responsible high government officials who were informed to look beyond the

limits of the present war and its weapons to the ultimate implications of these discoveries. This was a heavy responsibility. In a free country like ours, such questions should be debated by the people and decisions must be made by the people through their representatives. The people of the country must be informed if they are to discharge their responsibilities wisely.

And Discussion Began . . .

"Gentlemen, is the atomic bomb good or bad for the world?" asked Chancellor Robert Maynard Hutchins at the University of Chicago Round Table discussion on "Atomic Force—Its Meaning for Mankind," which was broadcast over NBC stations on August 12, 1945.

The three participants in this round table represented the University of Chicago, which served as a principal center of fundamental research in the development of the atomic bomb, and which announced the establishment of a comprehensive program for studying the peacetime uses of atomic force. The University created two Institutes—one of nuclear study and one of metal study—with the appointment, among others, of two Nobel Prize winners, Harold Urey and Enrico Fermi.

The participants in the following discussion were Robert Maynard Hutchins, Chancellor of the University; R. G. Gustavson, scientist and Vice President and Dean of Faculties of the University of Chicago, and former president of the University of Colorado; and William F. Ogburn, sociologist and foremost American scholar of the social changes wrought by invention and technology.

Mr. Hutchins' question was addressed to Mr. Gustavson, who replied:

GUSTAVSON: On the day the bomb was dropped, I met the Director of the University Laboratory which helped to develop the atomic bomb. His first words were:

"This is a very sad day for us. Let us hope we have not placed dynamite in the hands of children."

HUTCHINS: Well, Ogburn, was it wise to use this bomb against Japan?

OGBURN: By ending the war, it saved more lives than were lost at Hiroshima.

HUTCHINS: Wasn't the war going to end, anyway?

OGBURN: But when? The Japanese Minister to Sweden said in this morning's paper that the atomic bomb brought the plea for peace. We can't have peace or progress without paying the cost, as Charles Darwin showed.

HUTCHINS: But this is the kind of weapon that should be used, if at all, only as a last resort and in self-defense. At the time this bomb was dropped, the American authorities knew that Russia was going to enter the war. It was said that Japan was blockaded and its cities burned out. All the evidence points to the fact that the use of this bomb was unnecessary. Therefore, the United States has lost its moral prestige.

GUSTAVSON: At the very least, we might have used another method. We might have demonstrated the effectiveness of the bomb by calling our shot in advance, by giving the Japanese an opportunity to watch us drop a bomb on an uninhabited part of Japan and then calling upon Japan to surrender.

HUTCHINS: Well, perhaps the future is more important than the past. Ogburn, as a social forecaster, what seems most important to you about the atomic bomb?

OGBURN: Well, I think this may very well be, Hutchins, the most important invention of all time. The explosive energy in the atomic bomb undoubtedly brightens the prospect for abolishing war, in my opinion. But if, in addition, atomic energy is harnessed, I think it will usher in the Atomic Age and may produce sweeping changes comparable to those of the Industrial Revolution which was brought in by steam.

The Industrial Revolution, we all know, created our cities, made nations bigger, shifted world powers, weakened the family as an organization, revolutionized agriculture, built up a perfectly enormous industry, and led to the creation of the most powerful central governments the world has ever known.

HUTCHINS: Gustavson, you're a scientist. What do you say?

GUSTAVSON: I would say the bomb teaches us the value of fundamental research. The work done by Professor Fermi and others on the effect of the neutron on the uranium atom was research carried out from the point of view of curiosity, for the general purpose of increasing human knowledge. There was no specific purpose of producing atomic energy, and certainly no intention of producing world-shattering bombs. The basic work was an attempt to find out something about the universe in which we live.

To me, that is the important lesson. That is the way all really important discoveries are made.

HUTCHINS: My own conviction is that the moral burden which this discovery places upon the peoples of the earth and the necessity of a world organization to control this force are most important.

Well, let us take up, in order, the social and industrial consequences, the implications for research, and the impact of this discovery on war, peace, and world organization.

OGBURN: Let us first see what we are talking about, gentlemen. If we are talking (a) about the explosive capacities of uranium only—which is, by the way, the only thing that is known definitely and publicly—that is one thing. If we are talking (b) about harnessing power from uranium and regulating its flow through machines —which is something that I have not yet heard we can do definitely—then the social consequences, of course, will be very much greater. But if we are talking (*c*) about releasing atomic energy not from uranium alone, but from more and more abundant materials, such as clay or common water, for instance—and of this I am skeptical as well as uninformed—then no human imagination can encompass its consequences, in my judgment.

GUSTAVSON: Ogburn, this is the most important discovery that has been made since the discovery of fire. It is more important than all the inventions since the Industrial Revolution combined. This discovery is the answer to the dream of the alchemist. We are dealing here with a transmutation of elements, the destruction of matter, the liberation of tremendous quantities of energy—energy the intensity of which defies description. For example, when dynamite explodes you have an intensity represented by about four volts. Now we are talking about something of the order of 200,000,000 volts.

OGBURN: That is impressive—but, Gustavson, inventions have nearly always been overpromised. Ninety-five per-cent of them never materialize at all. Take, for instance, the singing wire or the talking book, which were invented in the 1890's. They have not been put to public use yet. Or take another invention—that of gas warfare, which put fear in our hearts and was certainly overpromised twenty-five years ago, at the end of the first World War. It has never materialized up to its promises.

My calculation shows that it takes on an average of about 35 years for an invention to materialize, and sometimes it takes two or three hundred years, or longer.

All inventions of the past that I have studied have been resisted. Take prefabricated housing, for instance. We could have had it fifty years ago. But instead it has been resisted by the building trades, certain real-estate interests—and, of course, the mortgage companies: they don't want it.

GUSTAVSON: It seems to me that the trend today, however, is away from resistance and towards too ready acceptance of new things. As a people, we are credulous and volatile, rather than skeptical and slow to change. Take vitamins and nylon, for example.

OGBURN: But, Gustavson, we mustn't allow ourselves to begin talking like Jules Verne.

HUTCHINS: This time, Jules is justified.

OGBURN: Yes, but if Jules Verne were sitting on the Chicago Round Table today, he would be using the atomic bomb to organize a war on the planet Mars.

But there are many, many forces which would be changed. Civilization is really a complicated mass of interrelationships like a huge piece of machinery. You can't change one part without changing many parts. To bring in a regulated atomic power means, for instance, changing railroads, electric power systems, banks, factories, and many other types of social organization. All this takes time. We don't get inventions adopted overnight.

GUSTAVSON: We may not get inventions overnight, Ogburn, but we do know certain things about this discovery: We do know that we get out of it incredible heat, incredible power, incredible radioactivity, and new elements.

OGBURN: Yes—but, Gustavson, there is another factor, it seems to me, which slows up the use of inventions. An invention will not be used if it costs too much. President Truman told us, for instance, that atomic energy cannot compete in terms of cost with coal or electricity at this stage. The atomic bombs cost, it is reported, one billion dollars apiece. You can't pick up a piece of U-235 as cheaply as you can pick up a piece of coal and put it into a furnace. The question still is whether the costs will be brought down low enough—and this is something we certainly do not know yet.

Then, let us assume that we have a fundamental discovery—

HUTCHINS: But if we have a fundamental discovery, we have one in a very early stage. What are the social consequences that you, as a social scientist, can reasonably foresee, even at this stage?

OGBURN: I have been trying to argue that we need not get a case of the jitters; that inventions, although they disturb our sense of security, have a way of developing slowly against what we call social inertia, in the face of resistances arising from the complicated nature of our society, and with the handicap of high costs.

But to answer your question, Hutchins: If we cannot abolish war, we can count on a considerable effect on the layout of our cities and on city planning. Cities have been dispersed, as you know, by the automobile and the railroad—and more recently, of course, by the bomber, which should disperse them even more. But if an explosive of this kind can reach them, cities will undoubtedly be dispersed and spread outward. This is a tendency already under way.

GUSTAVSON: Can we look forward to more leisure?

OGBURN: Any great new use of energy has the potentialities of reducing—and even abolishing, I may say—physical toil. I think we might even look forward into the future to factories without any laborers in them at all. But, of course, this will all come slowly.

GUSTAVSON: Couldn't we have technological unemployment on a scale we have never dreamed of?

OGBURN: We could—if the inventions came quickly enough. But most inventions produce technological unemployment only temporarily. Unemployment in the main is really caused by business fluctuations and by population changes. I have calculated, for instance, that only fifteen per-cent of the depression of the 1930's was technological.

GUSTAVSON: Remember that this is a fundamental discovery of very fundamental character. It could affect our whole industrial civilization.

HUTCHINS: Well, what about the effect on the standard of living?

OGBURN: It will make the Atomic Age an age of abundance. I am particularly excited, though, about the possibilities for transportation, which I have been studying recently. If atomic energy could be put in a rocket—and that doesn't seem so very difficult—and if these rockets could be kept cool and slowed near their destination, it is perfectly possible, I think, to travel 3,000 miles an hour. This would mean we could leave New York one day and arrive in China the day before.

HUTCHINS: Who's talking like Jules Verne now?

GUSTAVSON: Let us not forget that the bomb is the end product of a series of discoveries. In all probability, the liberation of atomic power in a fashion that can be controlled for industry will be much simpler than making the bomb.

HUTCHINS: I am interested in the suggestion that this discovery will favor the big industries—at least in its present stage, where we have relatively rare materials and a relatively expensive process. How do you gentlemen feel about public versus private control of this material and this process?

OGBURN: Let me give some illustrations on this point: Most of the power inventions that we have now have developed big industries of the public utility type—electricity, railroads, aviation. These are certainly not the industries for small business.

I suspect that the development of atomic energy will be in this class. It will tend to strengthen the big industries. It is very likely, by the way, to speed us further on the road to serfdom, as the term is now used—to tend to reinforce movements towards monopoly and towards cartels—if, of course, we don't do something about it. But if it can be used in very small packages, then it may, of course, not accentuate this tendency. Most probably, however, it will put tremendous power in the hands of large industrial units. And that brings up the question: What are we going to do about it?

GUSTAVSON: It seems to me it will go about the way the development of power in general has gone. We have seen the government step into the power problem, to control our great water resources for the development of electrical power. It seems to me we are increasingly coming to the conclusion that anything so fundamental to our economic structure as electricity, or power in general, has to be something that is government controlled. The government would logically have a lot to say about the development and distribution of atomic power.

OGBURN: I agree. Military reasons, of course, are added to the economic reasons in this case.

HUTCHINS: You both feel, then, that on the military side there is no question that the government will have to continue in control of this process and in control of the material used in it; but if large industries are the only ones that are in a position to develop the process or exploit the material at the present time, then we shall have to have government regulation of those industries.

Gustavson, what are the implications of this discovery for medicine and for health and for biology?

GUSTAVSON: They are tremendous, of course. The radioactivity associated with all of this work has great possibilities for good and for harm. There will be industrial hazards, for example, in the new industries—exposure of workingmen to dangers which we never suspected before.

We are going to use these radioactive materials, too, in the study of disease processes. We are going to use them in attempting to follow the fundamental researches in biology. The implications for public health, as I have said, probably cannot be overstated.

HUTCHINS: Do you think that we may have as great a

revolution in medical treatment and in biological investigation as the revolution that we can see ahead of us in the physical sciences and in technology?

GUSTAVSON: There is no question about it.

HUTCHINS: We come, then, to the second main point on this round table, gentlemen: If the government has succeeded in creating a notable curse with two billion dollars and the concentrated effort of thousands of scientists over four or five years, why couldn't we ask that the government devote the same money and effort to the elimination of some of the already existing curses, such as cancer, influenza, venereal disease, unemployment at home, or starvation abroad?

GUSTAVSON: The important point here, Hutchins, is that while it is relatively easy to get large sums of money to study the cancer problem that you have suggested, it is by no means easy to get large sums of money to study the fundamental properties of living matter.

In the last analysis, the solution of the cancer problem will probably be a by-product of fundamental research on how the cell divides, why it divides. We should remember that the nucleus of the cell is just as important in biology as the nucleus of the atom is to nuclear physics. We should remember, as I said before, that when Professor Fermi did some of the fundamental work leading to the atomic bomb, bombs were the farthest thing away from his thinking.

Similarly, the cure for cancer will come indirectly, in my opinion, out of fundamental research, and probably not out of the study of cancer.

HUTCHINS: But doesn't this mean that such researches would have to be centered in universities, rather than in industry or under the auspices of the government?

OGBURN: Hutchins, the history of research has shown, in my judgment, that industry is interested primarily in applied researches. Government is interested, in the main, in contemporary applications. The only fundamental research that has been done of any significance has been done at the universities. Take, for instance, radio broadcasting and radar. They were dependent upon the discoveries, through pure research and pure science, of the Hertzen waves.

GUSTAVSON: After all, where did the government turn in its hour of great fear? It didn't turn to industry, and it didn't turn to itself. It turned to the universities.

OGBURN: The atomic bomb, Gustavson, has put to the universities the biggest challenge they have ever faced, in my judgment. We have to know what to do with this murderous weapon which we have created. Without a liberal education, and without spiritual education, it may become our master and our destroyer.

What the natural scientists do, you know, is to unleash these inventions which cause a reorganization of society, a reorganization of our political and our economic institutions and our social institutions—and always, of course (and this should not be forgotten), a re-evaluation of our ideologies.

But here we are, sitting around this table and trying to give answers in a half-hour when it can't be done. It took two billion dollars and three years, so we are told, to produce an atomic bomb. If the various social scientists had two billion dollars and three years of research, we could give better answers.

But I think maybe we ought to consider declaring a moratorium on all pure science and on the researches of all natural science development until the social sciences can tell us what to do about it and can catch up.

HUTCHINS: I understand you are not seriously suggesting a moratorium. You are simply suggesting that Gustavson and I should get out and raise two billion dollars for the support of social science research. We will be glad to do that.

OGBURN: Chicken feed, Hutchins, chicken feed. We need much more than that.

HUTCHINS: I should like to consider whether, even if you had two billion dollars for social science research, you could have any effect on society if society were not educated enought to accept the results.

OGBURN: That, of course, is a basic problem.

HUTCHINS: And whether, therefore, it isn't necessary for the university—and whether this isn't another of the responsibilities of the university—to develop liberal education for all.

GUSTAVSON: Quite right. Even Harvard and Yale and the University of Colorado, my former institution, have decided at last to devote themselves to general education as a preliminary to specialization. It would seem that this must be the trend, and it must be tremendously accelerated.

HUTCHINS: If we are going to have a society that knows what to do with these constant surprises from the physical scientists, we are going to have to have an entirely different level of general intelligence in the community from the one that we have been used to in the past.

OGBURN: That, Hutchins, is really the challenge of the atomic bomb, as I see it. The bomb, as we know, paralyzed Japan. But also I should like to note that the first week in the Atomic Age has given the rest of the world a very bad state of jitters, to say the least. But what we really fear, I think, is not the bomb so much as the unknown. But we need not fear it if we can control its development, control the knowledge, and use it consciously and competently for good, and not for evil.

HUTCHINS: Well, that brings us, doesn't it, to our last point, which is the military and political significance of atomic force?

OGBURN: It is an interesting fact that nations in the past, throughout the long history of mankind, have risen

and fallen pretty much on the basis of the inventions of
the past. England dominated the world during the nineteenth century. They did it because of the harnessing of
the first mechanical power—steam—which brought the Industrial Revolution to England fifty years before it came
to any other country or any other continent.

Prior to that, France and the other Western European
countries became powers by displacing the Mediterranean
countries because of the agricultural inventions of the
time, which made the river valleys of Western Europe
very powerful forces. But, before that, the Mediterranean
countries rose to power in antiquity because of another
invention—the boat.

Now there comes along a still more important discovery—the discovery of atomic energy. Will there be a re-
alignment of powers, of international powers?

HUTCHINS: Well, what I get out of what you have been
saying is that the United States is going to dominate the
world because the United States is sitting on this secret.

GUSTAVSON: If the United States tries to sit on this secret, it will make itself the most hated power on the face
of the earth. But you can't sit on this secret. If the history
of science shows anything, it shows that discoveries are
made practically simultaneously in several parts of the
world, that no single nation develops an idea of this
kind.

As you well know, Hutchins, if you look over the men
who are going to work at the University of Chicago in the
Institute of Nuclear Physics, you will find that they come
from practically all over the world—from Italy, from Hun-
gary, England, Canada, as well as the United States.

This bomb was a composite that grew out of the efforts
of many people. If any one nation attempted to isolate
itself scientifically, it would soon be outstripped by the
others, which would not be parties to the secrecy.

OGBURN: Brains, in the hereditary sense—as you biologists know, Gustavson—are pretty generally distributed evenly over the world. The thing we have to look out for, though, is this: What is the distribution of the natural resources of this new source of power? Where do we find uranium? In Colorado, in Utah, and in Canada. But it also exists in Czechoslovakia, in Africa, and in Russia. That puts it in the hands of what we call the peace-loving nations. May I say here that I hope they will continue to love peace.

GUSTAVSON: Your implication that the release of atomic energy is limited to uranium is open to question. In all probability, we shall learn to apply the process to ever more abundant elements. It seems to me that this discovery really equalizes the nations by placing atomic power, with all of its potentialities, in the hands of small nations. What we have done is the equivalent of placing a slingshot in the hands of David.

OGBURN: Not yet, not yet, Gustavson. The chances are that the difference between the small nations and the big nations will be increased, rather than diminished. That is what happened with the tank and the bomber. They practically killed off the small nations as effective factors in the distribution of power. The atomic bomb will very likely strengthen the big nation because, whatever the little nation can do, the bigger one can do it better and more quickly.

GUSTAVSON: But your assumption is that it takes a lot of airplanes and a tremendous amount of industry to do this sort of job. It is altogether possible that relatively small numbers of workers in a small country such as Denmark could develop all the facilities that are necessary without a single bomber—and with only a runway, say, a rocket, and an atomic bomb man in Copenhagen, you could destroy Berlin.

OGBURN: Still, I maintain that the big nations can still

produce bigger and better and quicker results. What do you think, Hutchins?

HUTCHINS: The first thing I think is that peacetime military training in the United States now becomes an irrelevant issue. You don't need a big army to operate an atomic bomb. You don't need much of an air force. Peacetime conscription is a soporific. We should not rely on large masses of half-trained men; we should pin our faith on scientific research.

GUSTAVSON: At the present stage, uranium is known to be distributed only in certain places. Manpower and industrial strength related to its use are, of course, important. The issue is whether, as scientific research proceeds, it will not result in the further distribution of power, which might bring the smaller nations back to the same level. But the upshot, in any case, is that the atomic bomb cannot be suppressed.

Ogburn, by talking about the abolition of war, did you mean something like the United Nations might abolish war by agreement, now that the atomic bomb has fallen?

OGBURN: Gustavson, it is the best chance to banish war we have had since the League of Nations—at least, to banish it for a time—and, I hope, for a very, very long time.

HUTCHINS: I don't follow you at all. After the last war, it was said that the airplane and the TNT bomb were going to be so horrible that nobody would ever fight again, and Hitler began to fight as soon as he saw that he had industrial resources and a political position adequate to give him a good chance of success. Isn't that always going to be the case? You are not going to abolish war merely by making it horrible.

GUSTAVSON: People are going to fight for whatever they think they can win. They always have, and they always will.

OGBURN: The Japanese apparently thought it was too

horrible. But don't misunderstand me. I am not saying that we can abolish war forever. About all we can do, I think, is to look forward about twenty or twenty-five years. The problem practically, though, is to make war more difficult. If the atom bomb has all the destructive capacities, it may be our golden opportunity.

HUTCHINS: We have always had this chance. The whole question is: What is at stake, and what are your chances? If a man has a chance to dominate the world through the control of atomic energy, that is a very large stake—and if he has, through the advances made by the scientists in his country, an opportunity to use this atomic force in such a way as to justify him in thinking that he has the edge on his enemies, he will take advantage of the situation and start another international conflagration. How are you going to prevent that?

Did I understand you to say that you thought we could have an international agreement which will either stop scientific progress in weapons or make every nation feel that it should never take advantage of such progress?

OGBURN: Such an agreement is not impossible, certainly.

HUTCHINS: The question is not whether it is impossible, but whether it would be effective. Up to last Monday, I must confess, I didn't have much hope for a world state. I believed that no moral basis for it existed, that we had no world conscience and no sense of world community sufficient to keep a world state together. But the alternatives now seem clear. One is world suicide. Another is agreement among sovereign states to abstain from using the bomb. This will not be effective. The only hope, therefore, of abolishing war is through the monopoly of atomic force by a world organization.

OGBURN: That is a thousand years old.

HUTCHINS: Remember that a French philosopher referred to the "good news of damnation"—doubtless on the theory that none of us would be Christians if we weren't afraid of perpetual hellfire. It may be that the atomic bomb is the "good news of damnation," that it may frighten us into that Christian character and those righteous actions and those positive political steps necessary to the creation of a world society—not a thousand or five hundred years hence, but now.

We Must Decide

Nathan Robertson of the Washington Bureau of PM reported the legislation being planned by Congressmen:

The atomic bomb is the most sensational of the Government's wartime scientific achievements, but it is only one of many. Thousands of others have resulted from the unprecedented concentration of research under Government direction and financing. Scientific progress has been advanced by many years.

These results have been achieved by Government financing of a huge research program which has cost about $700,000,000 a year in addition to the $2,000,000,000 spent developing and producing the atomic bomb.

The issue facing Congress is whether the Government should let this huge research program go to pieces after the war, or should make arrangements to continue it so this country can keep ahead, not only in research that affects national defense, but also in peacetime science.

Strong recommendations for the creation of an agency to continue a broad Governmental research program after the war have come from the Kilgore subcommittee of the Senate Committee on War Mobilization, and from a Presidential committee headed by Vannevar Bush, head of the Office of Scientific Research and Development.

Their recommendations are generally along the same line, although here are a few sharp conflicts.

Bills embodying both plans have been introduced.

The major conflict between the Kilgore and the Bush-Magnuson approaches to the problem of post-war research lies in the handling of patents resulting from Government research. Kilgore wants them to go to the Government for the benefit of the public. The Bush plan would permit patents to be owned by the private research institution that developed them at the Government's expense, reserving for the Government only the right to use them on a royalty-free basis.

The Bush plan is the one that has been followed in many of the wartime research projects financed by the Government. As a result, some of the most important wartime inventions will be locked up by private patents after the war instead of being open to the public.

We Must Organize for Control

Secretary of War Henry L. Stimson has appointed, with the knowledge of the President, an interim committee consisting of the Secretary of War, chairman; James F. Byrnes, Secretary of State; Ralph A. Bard, former Under Secretary of the Navy; William L. Clayton, Assistant Secretary of State; Dr. Vannevar Bush, director of the Office of Scientific Research and Development and president of the Carnegie Institution of Washington; Dr. James B. Conant, chairman of the National Defense Research Committee and president of Harvard University; Dr. Compton, chief of the Office of Field Service in the O.S.R.D. and president of the Massachusetts Institute of Technology; and George L. Harrison, special consultant to the Secretary of War and president of the New York Life Insurance Co. Harrison is alternate chairman of the Committee.

Mr. Stimson explained that:

The committee is charged with the responsibility of formulating recommendations to the President concern-

GEORGE L. HARRISON

JAMES BRYANT CONANT

ing the postwar organization that should be established to direct and control the future course of the United States of America in this field, both with regard to the research and developmental aspects of the entire field and to its military applications.

It will make recommendations with regard to the problems of both national and international control. In its consideration of these questions, the committee has had the benefit of the views of the scientists who have participated in the project. These views have been brought to the attention of the committee by an advisory group selected from the leading physicists of the country who have been most active on this subject.

This group is composed of Dr. J. R. Oppenheimer, Dr. E. O. Lawrence, Dr. A. H. Compton, and Dr. Enrico Fermi. The interim committee has also consulted the representatives of those industries which have been most closely connected with the multitude of problems that have been faced in the production phases of the project.

Every effort is being bent toward assuring that this weapon and the new field of science that stands behind it will be employed wisely in the interests of the security of peace-loving nations and the well-being of the world.

We Must Co-operate

Prime Minister Clement R. Attlee has pledged British co-operation with President Truman's proposal that the secret of the atomic bomb be guarded until complete control of the devastating weapon is assured. The Prime Minister said (as reported by the Associated Press):

"It is the intention of His Majesty's Government to put all their efforts into the promotion of the objects . . . foreshadowed and they will lend their full co-operation to that end."

We Must Use Existing Machinery

James T. Shotwell, Chairman of the Commission to Study the Organization of Peace, and Honorary President of the American Association for the United Nations, writing in the *New York Herald Tribune,* explained how atomic power has affected the United Nations Charter.

Some commentators have already risked the opinion that the atomic bomb has rendered useless all the plans of the charter of the United Nations for safeguarding international peace. Fortunately that is not the case. On the contrary, the charter was drafted upon a principle which makes possible an adequate directorate for the use of the atomic bomb both to police the world for peace and to insure its proper use in peacetime pursuits, for the whole structure of the United Nations Organization is functional. Each part is designed to meet a particular need and the organs which it created or indorsed are adjustable to the practicable purposes in each case.

The problem of security can now at last be adequately dealt with, for war has become too dangerous an enterprise for any civilized nation to risk its existence by the use of so great and incalculable forces. The atomic bomb is an ultimatum upon war. It also places wholly new responsibilities upon the peoples and governments which will have to adjust themselves to the conditions of lasting peace.

Atomic energy will have to be outlawed in the uses of destruction, but it will have an ever-increasing, and illimitable horizon in peace-time pursuits. The direction and control of these beneficent operations will have to be as definitely international as the controls for the prevention of war. Science, which was slowly making the world interdependent—although we thought the pace was fast enough—has now suddenly made isolation wholly impossible. The interplay of industry, agriculture, and commerce throughout the world will be necessary for the prosperity of any one part of it, and the location and capacity of the productive centers in which atomic energy will be used is a matter of concern to all the world.

Therefore the work of the San Francisco Conference in the field of economic and social organization will prove of the utmost importance in the coming years, more important by far than the provisions for the prevention of war, because the atomic bomb will inevitably take care of that. On the other hand, the structure of the organization of peace contains a whole series of organs, each of which will take into account in its particular field the revolution in industry, which will take place when atomic energy is harnessed to the work of the world. The conference in San Francisco, therefore, did better than it knew when it created under the Assembly an Economic and Social Council to co-ordinate the work of "specialized agencies" in all the major fields of human interest. It stands to reason that one of the most important of these specialized agencies will have to be a special commission for dealing with the development of the peace-time uses of atomic energy.

The Atlantic Charter referred to the problem of raw materials and the need for a just allocation of them among the nations. Here is the greatest economic possession in all the world. The commission to deal with it should be composed of the leaders of industry, agriculture, and commerce, along with scientists and other outstanding intellectual figures, whose duty will be to study the advance in scientific discoveries and to apply them for the welfare of all.

There should also be national bodies of a similar nature in each of the two great fields, security and welfare. The problems are not those which can be solved either by laymen in government offices or by scientists alone.

Neither can they be left to the anarchy of uncontrolled competitive forces. Each step in the development must be watched and known and brought within the sphere of law, both national and international.

The details of a plan such as this will need careful study, but the arrangements for securing that study and a stand-still agreement among the nations to await its termination are inescapable responsibilities at the present time.

We Must Act

One of the first opinions handed down by a body expressly created to decide matters of international justice concerned the use of the atomic bomb, which the Japanese insisted was illegal. (Reported by Edward Tomlinson over NBC on August 11th.)

We may be in doubt as to what should be done with Hirohito, but some of the most learned among our neighbors are not. The so-called "Son of Heaven" is, according to the highest legal and juridical opinion in the Americas, just another war criminal. This is the opinion expressed by the Inter-American Juridical Committee, which has been meeting in Rio de Janeiro.

The committee has been engaged in a long study of the subject of war crimes and war criminals. This study and opinion was called for in a resolution adopted at the recent Inter-American Foreign Ministers Conference in Mexico City.

Yesterday, the committee announced its long-awaited findings. The report, signed by delegates of Brazil, Mexico, Chile, the United States, and others would make the Japanese emperor subject to public trial before the world, along with the war criminals of Nazi Germany and Fascist Italy.

This report of the Inter-American Juridical Committee

declares that: "The head of a state that engages in a war of aggression is criminally liable and subject to the judgment of an international tribunal."

The committee also declared that the atomic bomb is a lawful instrument of war, while the flying bomb, like the German V-bomb, is unlawful. The United States member, Dr. Charles G. Fenwick, stated the committee's position, saying that the atomic bomb can be guided to its target, so as not to hit unidentified or non-military areas, but the V-bomb cannot.

We Must Be Realistic

Hanson W. Baldwin in the *New York Times* on August 13th, called for a new appraisal of our nation's defense.

The most important news last week—and not only last week, but the most important news since the Industrial Revolution—was not the collapse of Japan, not the end of the war, but the first use of atomic energy in history.

In a fraction of a second the atomic bomb that dropped on Hiroshima altered our traditional economic, political, and military values. It capped a revolution in the technique of war that started in the first World War—with the development of gas, the tank, and the plane—a revolution that now has swept many of our military ideas and instruments into the limbo of the past, and that forces immediate reconsideration of our entire national defense problem.

In stating the problem that now confronts us it is essential to avoid over-simplification or exaggeration. Atomic fission, although by far the greatest development of the war, is only one of many technological advances, each so startling as to warrant the description: "revolutionary." The bombs that were dropped on Hiroshima and Nagasaki were the first in history—and hence, surprise added immeasurably to their effects. Terrible damage was done to both cities but neither was completely destroyed. The radius of destruction of the atomic bomb —tremendous though it is—has a limit, and that radius seems to be somewhat cushioned and confined, or at least restricted, by hills and mountains. Bomb shelters very deep within the earth might withstand the blast.

The atomic bomb alone—as it is today—is not the sole agent, although it certainly is the principal one, that compels a complete re-evaluation of the principles and organizational procedures upon which our whole system of national defense is founded. There are other factors that also are compelling:

(1) The *potential*, rather than the *present*, military effectiveness of atomic fission. The bombs now used probably are a crude beginning, and we already have been told that future bombs will be far more destructive and powerful. As against this factor, however, must be set the certainty that surprise will not again be as great as at Hiroshima, and that defensive measures of some sort— even if only dispersion—will be the fundamental objective of every power.

(2) Rocket propulsion. The German V-2 stratosphere rockets, which bombarded London, could not be intercepted by any means now known. They traveled far faster than sound, and arced sixty to seventy miles into the air. The Germans were developing a transatlantic rocket when they surrendered, and in time, perhaps with the aid of atomic energy engines, transpacific rockets will be developed. These rockets so far are inaccurate, but science has it within its present power to correct that inaccuracy. It does not yet have it within its power to stop the rockets, once launched. Other rocket developments have, in themselves, changed the art of war.

(3) Electronics. Radio and radar have made it possible for man to "see" far beyond his visual range, and to

pull hidden "strings" that actuate planes, tanks, ships, and so on by remote control. The science of navigation has been revolutionized by radar, and attack on a target, as for instance by a radar-controlled glide bomb, can be accurately accomplished by a man miles from the scene.

(4) Aerodynamics. The great development of the plane has made conventional terrain barriers—and even seas—of far less strategical importance than formerly. The jet engine, still encountering metallurgical and other difficulties in this country opens a whole new science of reaction propulsion and introduces problems such as compressibility which, when solved, will enable planes to travel far faster than sound.

(5) Marine engineering. At the end of the war the Germans had developed a new type U-boat with a new chemical engine and streamlined hull which, equipped with the Schnorkel air intake tube, could remain under water at periscope depth for weeks continuously and had the phenomenal under water speed of twenty-one knots or faster.

These are only some of the developments that have so profoundly altered the art of war that familiar concepts and implements and tactics—new and radical though they seemed one or two years ago—now are obsolescent.

A trend that began in the first World War now has come to a climax—the offensive has triumphed over the defensive, perhaps not an ultimate triumph but a smashing and conclusive one at least for the forseeable future. Long-range rockets with atomic warheads now can span oceans and demolish cities overnight, and there is no present known way of preventing this.

But, lest the development of the rocket and the atomic bomb be oversimplified and classed as the ultimate victory of air power, it should at once be said that this is not true. It is rather the triumph of "push-button" war. General H. H. Arnold has said that this may be the last war of the pilots, and that probably is true. For obviously there will be far less reason for the gigantic bomber tomorrow than there was yesterday. Pilotless planes and long range rockets, with atomic warheads can do the mass bombardment hitherto accomplished only be gigantic fleets of giant bombers—probably the most expensive instruments of war known to man.

The introduction of the atomic bomb and companion developments in other fields therefore have changed completely our concept of air power, just as it has even more profoundly modified our concept of land armies and surface navies.

This does not necessarily mean that piloted planes and surface forces henceforth will be useless—although it does mean than war fundamentally has become a battle between opposing factories and laboratories—a direct struggle to break the enemy's home front. It may mean that the total character of war, which we hitherto had thought had approached its ultimate, will be even more total, and that all civilians may have to become soldiers.

It certainly means—change. Piloted planes may well be useful for specialized purposes—precision bombing, reconnaissance, and most particularly as transports for airborne armies. Ships still will need surface warships for protection and submarines still will ply the under waters, as long as ships ply the seas at all. Land armies still will be needed to follow up, to occupy, to root out "subterranean man" from his caves and caverns, and to organize and govern.

But sea power, land power, air power must profoundly change in character and concept, for the first line of defense tomorrow will be the directors of "push-button war"—the men who fling gigantic missiles across the seas. Behind them as a second "bombardment wave," will come shorter-range, more accurately controlled missiles, piloted planes, radar-controlled glide bombs and so on.

Behind them may fly the airborne land armies—small but highly trained—to mop up and to occupy. But as far as we now can see—and at the moment the range of our military vision is veiled—conventional armies, navies, and air forces as we now know them are obsolescent.

All these considerations cast grave doubts on what is known of the plans for our post-war national defense organization. Giant warships, mass armies, peacetime conscription, and tremendous bomber fleets have lost some of their military meaning. Advanced bases, too, have less importance; transoceanic missiles can by-pass them. Terrain barriers and seas have smaller meaning; the very basis of some of our strategic assumptions of the past must be challenged.

We must try to think in broad new terms, by yardsticks hitherto beyond the reach of man.

There will be grave danger, however, of resistance to this process. There will be demands for conventional planning; there will be strenuous efforts by the Army and the Navy—and the air forces of both services—to cling to the outmoded and the outworn; there will be the traditional military reluctance to depart from time-tested tactics and techniques. And there is danger that this resistance will hamper what must now have A-1 military priority—the development of a new and modern national defense system.

The great post-war military problems that confronted us before the atomic bomb dropped still are with us —the unified single department of defense; bases; peacetime military training; size and composition of Army and Navy; function of ground, sea, and air forces; research and development and production. They still are problems, but they must be completely recast in the light of the technological revolution in war.

That reconsideration cannot be left to the armed services themselves, unless biased and uncoordinated planning—planning in no sense commensurate with the advance in warfare—is to result. Research—intensive research, to learn, for instance, how to control (if that be possible), and how to defend against, the atomic bomb—is vital for the security of the country and of the world. It must be coordinated research. But with research must be conducted a study into the effects of the technological revolution upon all our national defense policies.

This is a big job for big minds, but it is the most important military job—perhaps the most important job—of the immediate post-war period. It should be undertaken by the leading citizens of the nation, organized in a commission, appointed by the President and/or the Congress. This commission should have technical advisers from the military services and other branches of Government, but it should be civilian in composition, impartial, objective, and judicial. It should have full access to the facts of the technological revolution in war. Its comprehensive studies should embrace all aspects of our postwar national defense problem and should correlate defense policies with foreign policies. Such a job is pressing and the creation of such a commission—or some other form of fact-finding body—one of the imperatives of the immediate future.

For such a study—made in the full light of the explosion at Hiroshima heard 'round the world—will do more than save us billions in defense costs and in wasted effort.

The secret of the atomic bomb will not always be ours alone. The Germans were ahead of us in pure research; our mass production in development and applied research beat them. After V-E Day in Europe, a German cargo submarine, bound for Japan, which surrendered to our forces in the Atlantic, was found to have (among other things) a cargo of uranium abroad, and the meaning of that is clear, for U-235, the terrible explosive of the atomic bomb, is derived from uranium. The Russians also have able scientists. We shall not always have the atomic bomb to ourselves.

Such a re-study of our entire national defense program, therefore, is essential for the security of the nation, and to an efficient, modernized, and economic national defense.

The Challenge to Wisdom

The Reverend Robert I. Gannon, S. J., President of Fordham University, defined destiny's challenge.

We have nothing but applause for the pure intelligence that went into the perfecting of the atomic bomb. But the news of its success is appalling.

Such power of destruction would have been a social hazard even in the civilized thirteenth century. Our savage generation cannot be trusted with it at all. It is a triumph of research, but unfortunately it is also a superb symbol for the Age of Efficient Chaos.

Anne O'Hare McCormick, writing in the *New York Times,* stated the Promethean role of the United States:

The first reaction of the Allied world was relief that this engine of immeasurable destruction was not in the hands of the enemy, as it might have been if the Germans had been able to hold out another year. But in this relief was no elation; it was mixed with wonder, fear, and deep misgiving, for every man knows in his heart that the bomb that harnesses the fire of the sun and the sleeping forces of the earth itself to the business of war is an ultimatum to the human race. Make peace, it says, or perish.

The words spoken by the detonator make everything said about it sound hollow. Yet the statements of the President, the Secretary of War, Mr. Churchill, and the military officers who described the tests in New Mexico are solemn and weighty pronouncements. They are the utterances of men profoundly conscious of the gravity of the decision they took in approving the use of this last weapon to end the war. It is a weapon developed by the scientific brains of democratic nations, with the decisive help of great German pioneer research workers like Dr. Albert Einstein, Dr. Lise Meitner, and others whom Hitler rejected because they were "non-Aryan." It was launched under the aegis of democratic powers, the United States, Great Britain, and Canada. Not even Russia shares the knowledge of the formula and the process by which nature's most potent secret has been put at the service of man.

It was not launched lightly. The words of the democratic leaders express the solemn sense of responsibility. They fear for the use of the most thrilling and the most terrifying discovery of our time. They know that it depends on them whether it becomes a terrible boomerang or the ultimate force that will revolutionize international life. It depends on the democratic peoples. It is impossible to imagine any government spending $2,000,000,000 on a laboratory or any other experiment that would bring peace to the world. If nations used their brains and their wealth prodigally to win peace as they do to win wars, the story of the twentieth century—the most scientifically advanced and the bloodiest in history—might be different.

But perhaps the money, the team-work of scientists of many nations and the zeal that went into the almost god-like task of splitting the atom will turn out to be an investment in peace. It is recognized by everybody that the bomb must be one thing or another, an instrument of life or an instrument of death. It will not remain long the secret possession of the nations that invented it, but for the present, for the crucial interval when the world must be organized as an entity or divide into spheres of power, it is controlled by three democratic nations. Although many may deplore that it was used first by the United States, this fact underlines that in a special if not exclusive sense it is controlled by us. It is another sign and instrument of our power to shape the future of the world.

It is hard to foresee the consequences of the new force we have released. It changes the conception of armies, navies, and air forces, changes the face of war itself. It is obvious that if it is to continue to be a weapon when this war is over, whoever uses it first will be the winner. But the winner will preside over a dustheap.

Developed to its capacity, the atomic bomb makes peace imperative by making war impossible. Even if it is never used again as a carrier of death, it is the most unanswerable argument yet advanced for a community of nations leagued together for self-protection in the pursuit and maintenance of peace.

The Reverend Canon West, of the Cathedral of St. John the Divine, spoke of "the seeds of hate that now distress all mankind" and the impotence of knowledge without love of God and fellow man.

Scientific research and mechanical achievement are of positive importance to organized religion only insofar as men use them to minister to the welfare of mankind. For example, the church regards steel as properly used in the form of a chapel or a girder, but as improperly used when turned into a weapon of offense. Electricity as properly used in light and therapy, and improperly used in an electrocution. The problem isn't steel or electricity, but man. No sane person regards war as a good thing. It may occasionally be necessary, but it is at best surgical, never curative. We are not, therefore, debating the particular use to which atomic force is being put. That seems to be nothing other than a vastly accelerated process of destruction which differs from ordinary bombing only in terms of efficiency. The remarkable thing is that seemingly for the first time our people have become aware of the horror which is total war. The full enormity of this human destruction is now dawning on the minds of our fellow countrymen, but the morality involved in a world war is the same involved in a small war, or even in a private war. Whosoever is angry with his brother already carries the seed of hate which is now distressing all mankind. From the religious point of view, the horror of this present sorry business will pale before worse things to come unless all men decide that plowshares and pruning hooks are of more permanent value than swords and spears. Constant deaths and constant rebirths are conditions to which religion is accustomed, but whether it be of an individual or of an era, such death and rebirth are thought of in moral terms. That these new scientific developments will produce a new kind of mechanical age seems certain. That new customs and habits will rise as new living conditions is equally certain. But the end or rebirth of civilization depends on man's ability to exert moral judgment in their application. From the religious point of view the true height of any standard of living is determined by the degree to which material knowledge is subordinated to spiritual control. All the factual knowledge and all the physical experience in the universe do not necessarily constitute a knowledge of the truth. These data of the creative world have to be interpreted in terms of love for God and for one's neighbor, before such knowledge may be called truth. Search for such truth we believe to be man's vocation, and it will always be found as identical with that truth which shall make men free.

(From "The Atomic Bomb—The End or Rebirth of Civilization?" a symposium presented over WNEW, New York.)

Dr. Lise Meitner and Mrs. Franklin D. Roosevelt spoke of woman's place in science and woman's responsibility for seeing to it that our new power is used to conserve life, rather than destroy it.

Dr. Meitner spoke from her home in Leksand, Sweden, the country to which she fled after being exiled from Germany because of her Jewish origin. Mrs. Roosevelt spoke from the National Broadcasting Company's newsroom, in New York City.

MRS. ROOSEVELT: When I read the dramatic story of the way in which this new discovery had been started and that a woman had played such an important part in it, it gave me a feeling of great responsibility. It is a tremendous force and, if a woman was given the opportunity to discover it, certainly other women throughout the world have an obligation to see that it is used now to bring the war to a close and to save human lives, and that in the future it is used for the good of all mankind and not for destructive purposes.

I wonder if I might ask Dr. Meitner what her feeling was when she first heard of the dropping of the bomb and realized it might bring this destructive war to a close.

DR. MEITNER: Women have a great responsibility and they are obliged to try, so far as they can, to prevent another war. I hope that the construction of the atomic bomb not only will help to finish this awful war but that we will be able, too, to use this great energy that has been released for peaceful work.

MRS. ROOSEVELT: Thank you, Dr. Meitner. Women are conservers by nature. You, as a scientist, must feel a great satisfaction at every new advance in science; but, as a woman, you must feel a great desire to see this advance used to preserve and improve the life of the world. When reading the news, I could not help but think what it must mean to you who started this great force coming into the world. Can you think of any way in which you believe it should be controlled, Dr. Meitner? Should it be internationally controlled? Should it be controlled by scientists? How can we best, in your view, use it or control it for the good of mankind?

DR. MEITNER: I hope that by the co-operation of several nations it will be possible to do so, to come to better relations among all the nations, and to prevent such horrible things as we have had to go through in the last few years.

MRS. ROOSEVELT: I hope that you can inspire women to an inflexible determination that they will have their share in building a peaceful world, because the women of all the countries of the world want to see their children profit by this new discovery. Many people today are afraid of it, afraid of the things that may happen if we, as human beings, cannot rise to the opportunity of using it for the best possible purposes.

DR. MEITNER: I hope that we will fulfill these wishes and will be able to have cooperation around the world.

MRS. ROOSEVELT: Dr. Meitner, I hope that some day we in the United States will have the pleasure of seeing you here just as we saw Madame Curie and that we may feel your greatness as we felt her greatness, for you have shown great courage and I think every woman is proud of what you have done.

The deathless yearning to know—and the will to peace are reflected in an editorial in the *New York Times*.

But in this shock that ran like an earthquake around the world there is room for hope, room for dreams of a nobler future for mankind. The atomic bomb was perfected for war, but the knowledge which made it possible came out of man's purest and most disinterested strivings.

It came out of the deathless yearning to know and to use the gifts of nature for the common good. It came out of man's struggle to liberate himself from ignorance, to master his destiny, to lift the heavy burden of meaningless toil. This new knowledge can still be used for such purposes. It can bring to this earth not death but life, not tyranny and cruelty but a divine freedom. What dazzling gifts the science which split the atom can offer to the heavily laden everywhere! To take one instance, what cannot this science do for the millions of China and India, bound for so many ages in sweat and hunger to the wheel of material existence!

We have only to carry out the resolve, which surely every humane person on earth must have felt when he heard last Monday's news, that with the surrender of Japan this device must never again be used in war because there must never again be war. Is this torn and embittered world capable of living up to such a resolve? It has to be—or die. The San Francisco Charter is a beginning. All our hopes and strivings are only a beginning. The tramp of doom is at our doors but the stars of an eternal aspiration still shine.

The mysteries that have been solved do not reveal the inner secret of the universe, nor destroy our reverence in the presence of powers we cannot control. Bewildered humanity, with this awful instrument in its hands, may feel the age-old impulse to pray—and rising from its knees to work humbly and unselfishly for the perpetual peace that is now our only salvation.

"We can think . . . the atomic bomb proves it. But we must think about the affairs of men as well as we think about force and matter. We must think our way out of war and into the new Age," warns Lyman Bryson in a broadcast over CBS.

Monday night, when the news came, I was talking with

one of the scientists who has been in on the secret from the start. He told me nothing, of course, that has not been in the newspapers, because what he knows are government secrets. But I asked him how many people were in on the whole story. His answer was that no single person really knows the whole story. He said that there was probably no one person, not even one, who could give an accurate account of the whole business of the work that has been done in the United States and in Canada. If all the blueprints and machinery were destroyed, he said, it would take the combined knowledge of at least two hundred scientists and engineers to reconstruct the whole process. It is not, you see, something that a spy could steal. It is not a secret but a whole complicated organization of secrets. And it would not take another two billion dollars, but it would take more money than any but the richest nations can afford.

The layman's mind is completely baffled trying to guess what is being done in those immense sheds and laboratories where hundreds of thousands of men and women have been busy for many months. We cannot imagine what is being done there any more than we can follow the cryptic jugglings of mathematical figures that go before the work in the sheds. But it is good to know that these secret processes are not something that any madman can pick up and use to blow up the world. The atomic bomb is a great achievement of co-operation. Only co-operation by very highly trained men could make it work. And only co-operation among these men and with other men of wisdom and good will can ever put the scientific principles of atomic energy to good use.

There are some who will still think of it as possibly the death of civilization. The second thought of nearly everyone has been not joy because such great force may now be harnessed for our use but fear—fear of the threat to our lives, and fear that it will never be used for good.

This fear of destruction is not new. This is not the first time that new forces of destruction, fiercer and more mighty than any ever known before, have been loosed upon civilized mankind. In every case there has been a shudder and then recovery—and then indifference. In our lifetime, many of us can remember the threat of the submarine, death from underseas—and the airplane, death overhead.

In fact, the history of warfare is the history of decisive changes in the destinies of nations made by the invention of new weapons. Nearly thirteen hundred years ago, the Greeks of Byzantium had a kind of chemical warfare by which they set the ships of their enemies aflame, the Greek Fire whose secret we have lost. And gunpowder came into Europe six centuries ago, completely changing the balance of military power. In more recent generations, we have been more inventive. The tempo increases. In the war between the States, here in America, explosive shells were first fired from artillery and the old navies were made useless overnight. Iron plates had to be invented to protect ships against shellfire.

In the time of the war between the States, also, we got the first torpedoes that could move through the water on their own power. In the first World War came the submarines, and poison gas, and airplanes, and tanks. And everything was swifter and bigger and more deadly.

And in this is another point to be noted—that the inventions of new weapons of offense lead to new forms of defense almost keeping up—almost, but not quite. In spite of all the inventions of defense, wars do now destroy more, kill more women and children, level more homes, and threaten more millions with the aftermath of starvation and disease.

Each time we make a new weapon, we shudder and then forget. It is even possible that tomorrow we may completely forget this excitement of today over the climax in death, the atomic bomb. But no one can ever say, just because we have recovered our courage, that we may not destroy ourselves.

The position of the United States in world politics, and our responsibility for using our bargaining power for good is not negated by this great bomb—it is made immensely greater. Both our power and our responsibility are greater. . . . We may now be sowing in Asia, and perhaps in other parts of the world as well, a fear of America, a fear of our ability to annihilate cities and men. . . .

This puts on the men who manage the foreign policies of our government an urgent duty. . . . The possession of this kind of lethal knowledge, whatever use we make of it, the mere threat of its use, makes use more than ever a decisive and responsible factor in deciding how the world shall go. This first danger, that the people of other countries will be afraid of America's military power, is one that we shall have to watch with great alertness and careful judgment for the next few years, while, if possible, the world settles in a pattern of peace.

There is another danger. There are signs of it everywhere. The clearest sign is in the state of mind of the man who says, as one said to me last night, "Well—this shows that science is evil. Science is destruction. That's what comes of training men as physicists and chemists and engineers. God help us if they run the world."

I know a good many scientists, and most of them have less desire to run the world than the average man. They would probably do about as good a job of it as is being done by statesmen and business men now. But that is not the point. The point is that this atomic bomb, this explosion of death over Japan, is a last and clinching proof of the fact that we think more effectively about material things than we do about our purposes, our ideals, our human behavior. . . . Our doubt, the very widespread and anxious doubt, comes from our fear that nobody will think as clearly, as bravely and as unselfishly about peace and war, about human affairs and human actions, as those men and women in the laboratories have thought about atoms. We can almost control the physical universe. Can we control ourselves? . . .

What we need is not less science but a more intelligent and a more humane use of physical science and more scientific thinking in other fields. A more loyal service to the ideals we know and do not practice would help in this, of course. But also beyond that we need better thinking. We need, if such a thing is possible, the same kind of thinking in managing men as we can show in managing atoms. Men have always lived at their peril. It has always been that kind of world. We can see now that our ambitions and our inventions have enlarged that peril progressively in these modern times. We have asked the chance to live dangerously. We can find our hope that we can manage this perilous business of life in the fact that the same kind of thinking that made the atomic bomb has also made the modern medicine that saves the lives of our men on the battlefield and in our hospitals. This same thinking has given us all the miracles of comfort and convenience and safety of modern living. Can we believe that we can also think our way through to peace?

Dorothy Canfield Fisher, writing in the *New York Herald Tribune,* asked whether we would behave like rats driven by murder-lust, or like men capable of the self-discipline which permits reason to rule.

Six miles away from the trial of the first atomic bomb in New Mexico, the impact of the explosion knocked men down as though by a blow from a giant fist. All of us, as by the same fist, are knocked down, spiritually and mentally, by that terrific event.

Those six-mile-away observers, felled to the ground, were not killed. Not yet. Shaken and trembling they were able to rise and face human life once more. Once more. And we too must face human life once more in a confused emotional tumult, part horror and remorse over the two examples of the destructiveness of the bomb, part incredulous joy over the news of the surrender of Japan and the end of the nightmare.

On hearing the news of the bomb, our impulse was to cry out, "No, no, no, we have no 'comments' to make. no opinions, no plans to suggest. Nothing in our human experience has prepared us to meet this crisis."

But that is not literally true. Some experiences in humanity's past are so strong, so well-proven, that even this thunderclap does not cast them down.

The very story of the invention and manufacture of the bomb is an experience which can leave no doubt in anybody's mind as to the prodigious ability of human beings when they work together. Here, in this fabulous transcending of individual human limitations by collective effort, is an element on the strength of which we can absolutely rely as we face the future.

On its strength. Not on the use to which that strength will be put. For we must not shut our eyes to the possibility that too many members of the human race may be like the race of rats, who would rather fight each other than live. A brown rat may have everything a rat can desire—food, shelter, freedom, mating. Let him catch sight of a black rat, and all that gives him satisfaction is burned to a crisp in his murder-lust. The plain fact is that we do not yet know whether our human race is too akin to the rat race to survive.

We must face that grisly possibility or tragically fool ourselves. Yet we have in hand a piece of proven knowledge (not a guess) about the ways of our human race. This is the knowledge of the overwhelming influence on human beings of training and tradition. One by one, elements in human nature which, only a short time ago used to be considered inherent and inevitable are recognized as acquired from teaching.

What modern biology has given us proof of, is that the genes which determine human personality are too inextricably mixed and distributed among human individuals, to attribute any special qualities exclusively to any racial group.

One of the things we now know (know in every sense of the word) is that there is only one race, of which we are all members.

This knowledge wipes out the possibility that those human beings who speak any one language should—or could —use the bomb to dominate the rest of the race, for any purpose. The mind of man and his ability to achieve by co-operative endeavor results which fabulously transcend his individual limitations, cannot be shackled, or gagged or blindfolded—not in the long run.

Even if we could monopolize knowledge of the bomb, an attempt to use it to get more power for part of humanity would not succeed. This we know from our human past. For it is not true that the atomic bomb is something new to man, and hence something for which our experience teaches us nothing. It is new only in degree. It is no more than a development of the clubs of the first men who fought each other. Then the man with a club could conquer the man without a club. Later men with rifles could conquer Zulus armed with spears.

The (chance) discovery of the bomb by English-speaking people a little ahead of others, means that it might be possible in the beginning for them to establish over other nations that power which was sought by the men with clubs. But one of the things we have learned which is not affected in the least by the discovery of the atomic bomb, is that such power could last but a short time, and then, like all other such attempts to dominate, would go down in chaos. We know, absolutely know that such an attempt would be a blind alley, and a short one.

And were that road of domination actually open to us, no decently responsible people would wish to follow it. The great majority of us, in our hearts' core, do not want that. What we honestly want is what the best plain people all over the world want, "to work together without fear or hate."

It is not a question of morals or of ideals. The simple brasstack reality is that we cannot advance into the future unless we hold hard to two things we know about ourselves. First that every one of us is born with destructive, fighting rat potentialities, but that these potentialities can be, if we so will, controlled and kept down by human effort. Second, that human beings can be trained into the disciplined ability to think and work together constructively, so brilliantly proved to be a possibility by the story of the invention and manufacture of the atomic bomb.

One world—or no world? Dorothy Thompson, in her Bell Syndicate column "On the Record," described the international conduct necessary to save humanity from itself.

The atomic bomb was not the product of British or American science, but the result of co-operative efforts of international scientists, the chiefs of whom by the grace of Adolf Hitler came into the world of the western democracies.

With this invention everything we have hitherto done or even considered as a means of preventing war is completely outmoded. Every concept of checking aggression is inadequate. When atomic energy is further developed, along with jet propulsion, no power or combination of powers can check any aggressive state that has this weapon, and no state, however aggressive it may be, will attack another state which has it. Man is not made to fight atomic energy or to go to war against the sun.

The concept of dividing the world into two or three great power spheres, each with strategical thises or thats is childish. The concept of Balance of Power becomes a fairy-tale. If Switzerland had this weapon, and the Soviet Union did not, Switzerland would be more powerful than the Soviet Union.

A political deduction as logical as the instinct of self-preservation can immediately be drawn from this greatest of all human discoveries: There must be a world state. There cannot be several states or spheres each with sovereign power to do as it likes, and each, and eventually all, in possession of this weapon in various stages of development.

In the hands of any one power it can become, even without being used, a blackmailing instrument against all human liberty; in the hands of all, and uncontrolled, it will spell doom for mankind. It is not enough, after this, to control German and Japanese laboratories and industries.

All the laboratories and industries of the earth must be controlled and that is possible only if the world is under one control. We cannot live politically in the seventeenth century and scientifically in the fiftieth.

But since the root cause of all wars is fear of losing or hope of gaining means of subsistence or wealth, this discovery, that ultimately, if canalized in that direction, can provide inexhaustible sources of energy for all mankind, ends all reason for war, and its consequences should be total and universal disarmament. America has the greatest opportunity to save the world ever offered any people. It will not be hers forever.

Frank Kingdon, before Japan had surrendered, told us in an address over WMCA, New York, that if our new-found power fell into the hands of any man or any group, freedom would be lost to the world.

Their feet are on the path toward acknowledging their defeat. How can they avoid it? Try to imagine a sitting of the Japanese cabinet. The little men come into a highly formalized room, their uniforms correct and glistening with the decorations of their offices. They solemnly follow the traditional rituals of their people as they greet each other and take their places. They are the concentrated essence of all that has been the old imperialistic and superstitious Japan. Then the Premier begins to talk. The Army and Navy chiefs make their reports. The air in the room goes stifling as the gloom deepens. You can almost feel the walls moving in on them, as they realize more and more that they are sitting in a little room at the center of a little land completely encircled by the moving armies of the whole outside world closing in on them. To the west, they hear the echoes of the guns of mightly Allied fleets pounding the shores of their homeland. To the south, they see a gathering cloud of Allied armies on Okinawa, only 325 miles from their southern island, and beyond these armies they see the massed reinforcements in the Philippines and the moving forces in Borneo. To the southeast, they look upon the Allied army and navy moving through Burma and up from the Bay of Bengal and the Indian Ocean. To the west they see the innumerable host of China, stoic, unconquerable, growing in military might. To the northeast, they hear the rumblings of the first thunder that is the beginning of the storm breaking on them from Russia. To the north, they look on islands in the power of still other Allied troops. And all the sea around them is a grave of their ships and a highway of their enemies. They dare not lift their eyes to the skies for comfort, for tragic as the sky has hitherto been, it now is the bearer of the most dreadful threat which men on wings have ever unloosed. They are men caught in such a net of doom as no others have ever faced since the waters of the Flood. Fanatical they may be, and as superstitious as they are fanatical, but even their illusion cannot clothe them in such a blindness as cannot see their fate. They may search their former hopes—that the Allies would divide against each other, that their enemies would grow weary of making war—but there is no consolation in them. They have nothing but the offer made them from Potsdam by the United States, Britain, and China, with which Russia is now associated, and that other Potsdam Declaration which, telling them the fate of Germany, blueprints for them the alternative to surrender. Yet they hesitate. Why? Because they are not thinking of Japan. These men speak not for a people but for a ruling class. They are spokesmen for feudal families, for the military caste, for financial and industrial privilege, for politicians and hereditary governors. Let the cataclysm shatter Japan, they will hang on to their power until the last. Theirs is the lust which destroys a people and threatens the world with unending war. They are the reason we cannot stop short of any surrender save unconditional surrender. The world is not safe until the power of such men over others has been totally and finally destroyed. While such men rule in Tokyo, other men in Washington, London, Moscow, and Chungking, trustees of mankind's future freedom, cannot withold any effort to obliterate them.

We have the power to do it. But that sentence comes from our lips not as a boast, but almost as a warning. Power is a ladder on which men can climb to the stars. Power is a pit through which men can fall into hell. The extremes of good and evil are in it. The surrender of Japan will bring us all immeasurable relief, but it will also plunge us into the severest test men and nations have ever faced. A new struggle will begin between the best and worst we are, for the final crucible in which the fate of humanity will be decided is the crucible of our own wills in which we make the decision of the use to which our power shall be put. Add to the staggering measurements of the atomic bomb that it generates heat of two trillion degrees Centigrade, that is, three trillion six hundred billion degrees Fahrenheit. For the brief second of its maximum strength, it is a man-created miniature sun, blasting every atom within its range to nothingness. Now think of what a hundred or a thousand such bombs might do. There were eight hundred superfortresses over Japan this week in one raid. If each of those had carried one atomic bomb, they would have carried the equivalent of one million, six hundred thousand superfortresses carrying ordinary bombs. If each had carried a full load of atomic bombs, the eight hundred would have carried destructive power equal to that of eight million carrying ordinary bombs. Our imaginations shudder at the possibilities, yet there can be no doubt that we shall advance in knowledge to the point where we can provide such loads. This is our power. We are like gods able to foresee a day when we can turn our planet into one vast flaming ball of fire consuming everything except itself. We are like gods, but tragically we are not godlike, and this chasm measures the test which humanity must face. Who is to own the patents which control this new power? I can imagine men who count progress in no terms except their own gain already sitting down to plot how they can corner the world's uranium, or how they can possess themselves of the key patents on which this discovery works. These are men who are themselves for sale and draw the natural conclusion that everything in the universe is. They are as alien to the future as the war-lords of Japan sitting in Tokyo. No private ownership on earth is fit to be trusted with possession of this new power. It belongs to the people, and the agencies which control it will have to be subject to the people's will. This is a social instrument to be socially owned, socially administered, socially used for the benefit of all. Who is to continue to develop it? Its beginning sets the pattern. It should be developed by the worldwide fraternity of scientists, working directly under public control. All of us surely realize that its secret cannot be long in the possession of a limited group of nations. It will stimulate research in other lands. The wise thing is to to realize this and plan its world-wide study. Britain invented the tank, but the Germans improved it. We invented the airplane but Hitler used it in the blitzkrieg. China invented gunpowder but the western nations perfected it. This new power is too great to trust to any such competition and provincialism. The only company of men fit to be trusted with its ownership, control, and development is the whole family of mankind acting together. The man has not yet been born who is fit to have absolute power over any other man. The group has not yet been found fit to rule another group. The only answer to this kind of world power is a new kind of world society.

Acknowledgments

POCKET BOOKS expresses its appreciation of the assistance and cooperation of the following organizations and individuals:

The United Press; *The New York Times;* The Press Association; *The Chicago Sun;* Acme Pictures; The Associated Press; *The New York Herald Tribune;* The National Broadcasting Company; the newspaper *PM; The Hartford Daily Courant;* The Blakiston Company; *The New York Sun;* Ives Washburn; The Columbia Broadcasting System; *The Saturday Evening Post; Harper's Magazine;* John J. O'Neill; Brandt and Brandt; Major George Fielding Eliot; United Features Syndicate; radio station WNEW; Captain Harry M. Davis; *The New York Times Magazine; The Journal of Commerce;* Science Service; James T. Shotwell; Lyman Bryson; Dorothy Canfield Fisher; Bell Syndicate; Frank Kingdon; Marion Cazier, Janet Sigley; Fay Utko; Nell Walls.

A LIST OF POCKET BOOKS